Contract Killers

Phillip and Robert King

B. T. Batsford Ltd, *London*

First published 1995

© Phillip and Robert King 1995

ISBN 0 7134 7925 6

A CIP catalogue record for this book is available from the British Library.

Typeset by Apsbridge Services Ltd, Nottingham.
Printed by Redwood Books, Trowbridge, Wiltshire
for the publishers,
B. T. Batsford Ltd, 4 Fitzhardinge Street,
London W1H 0AH

A BATSFORD BRIDGE BOOK
Series Editor: Tony Sowter

CONTENTS

INTRODUCTION

Many best-sellers are produced on the principle that nobody ever went broke through underestimating the intelligence or taste of the public. *Contract Killers* contains affectionate parodies of four master story-tellers who have enjoyed immense success despite ignoring that principle and most of the other time-honoured tips for producing blockbusters.

Agatha Christie once described herself as a sausage machine. But what a sausage! The sizzle which helped to sell a hundred million books was the charisma of a bald-headed Belgian who boasted his way through whodunits which had no gratuitous violence and no sex, gratuitous or otherwise. Poirot tortured his readers, by censoring the output of his little grey cells until the final chapter; his chronicler, Hastings, by treating him as an imbecile when he was merely an idiot; and his suspects, by goading them beyond endurance during his inevitable climactic ego trip. And, sacré bleu, the blighter did it all in Franglais! Seven decades after his creation, we are still enjoying the torture, and Poirot still knows everything – except the English for *mon ami*.

The phenomenal John Grisham promises to outsell every other author except Chairman Mao, who had a slightly unfair marketing edge. Aided by critical superlatives most thriller writers would kill for, the creator of *The Firm* has smashed publishing records by replacing our traditional heroes with *lawyers*. Dickens, who invented the best-seller, would have been outraged. His lawyers were double-dyed villains, who saved your money from your enemies in order to grab it for themselves. Mario Puzo claimed that a lawyer with a brief-case could steal more than a hundred men with guns. But a Grisham legal super-hero like Mitchell McDeere can defeat more men with guns than a hundred FBI agents.

When Selznick produced the film of *Gone With the Wind*, he was warned that nobody had ever made a nickel out of a Civil War picture. And the other economic indicators weren't much better. Margaret Mitchell's Pulitzer prize-winning rebuttal of *Uncle Tom's Cabin* had achieved a new dimension of political incorrectness. The ignorant, self-seeking, gold-bricking Scarlett O'Hara had little of the stuff from which conventional heroines were made, and the war-time profiteer and whorehouse proprietor, Rhett Butler, was an archetypal anti-hero, long before the breed became popular. Yet half a century later, the book is still a model of literary craftsmanship (if you disagree, read F. Scott Fitzgerald on the subject) and the four-handkerchief movie has drawn tears from a billion romantics.

Rejecting the glamourous best-seller world of international intrigue, Mario Puzo (the author we can't refuse) lures us into the constricted private club of *The Godfather*, where everybody knows everybody else and has a pretty good idea what the other *bastardos* are up to. Although the Corleones all have a provisional licence to kill, they plan their vendettas not over a Martini, shaken not stirred, but a Chinese take-away, eaten from cardboard cartons while sitting round a kitchen table. Meanwhile, Don Vito Corleone, benevolent despot, moral philosopher and everyone's favourite uncle, is pulling the strings which will protect his superbly ordered society from the effete liberalism of the outside world.

The authors are grateful to the four novelists, to Pamela and Matthew Granovetter and John Parnell for suggesting parody subjects, and especially to Shireen Mohandes, for her invaluable editing, research, criticism and bridge knowledge.

CONTRACT FOR MURDER

1
CONTRACT FOR MURDER

Chapter One

"En vérité, mon ami," said Poirot, from the depths of his comfortable chair," the little grey cells of the estimable Monsieur Culbertson may be almost the equal of my own."

I was accustomed to my friend's monumental ego and had become adept at deflating it with delicate shafts of irony.

"Surely, Poirot, that cannot be possible."

"Perhaps not," he replied judicially, "yet his approach forcing system has such method that, but for its several obvious deficiencies, I could imagine myself as its inventor."

"You really are confoundedly conceited," I remarked subtly.

"You think so, Hastings? Then regard this hand from the recent Culbertson – Sims match."

He gave me the bridge magazine he had been reading. and I studied the remarkable and complex auction from the 'Bridge Match of the Century'.

Love All. Dealer East

Josephine Culbertson
♠ AK10
♡ —
◇ AK1098642
♣ A2

Hal Sims
♠ QJ864
♡ K72
◇ J75
♣ 98

Dorothy Sims
♠ 9532
♡ QJ106
◇ —
♣ Q7643

Ely Culbertson
♠ 7
♡ A98543
◇ Q3
♣ KJ105

West	North	East	South
–	–	Pass	Pass
Pass	2◇	Dble	Rdbl
2♠	3♠	Pass	4♡
Pass	5♣	Dble	Rdbl
Pass	5NT	Pass	6♣
Pass	6◇	Pass	7◇
All Pass			

"The game forcing opening bid showed at least a semi-solid suit," Poirot continued. "The double by the audacious Madame Sims was a typical psychic bid, unmasked by Culbertson's redouble. Monsieur Sims' take-out gave *la belle* Josephine the opportunity to show first round control of spades, and the bids in hearts and clubs which followed were, I deduce, cue bids. Again, the incorrigible Dorothy intervened, with a double of the five club bid, and Ely's redouble showed second round control."

"Absolutely," I agreed, hoping to persuade the little Belgian that I had followed his rapid analysis. But I could not help wondering what Mrs Culbertson's five no trumps bid meant.

"But alas, Hastings, in the subsequent bidding, order gave way to chaos. Even *le bon* Ely confessed that he could not interpret his wife's five no trumps."

"But of course *you* can," I smiled.

"*Mais oui.* I have written to the Culbertsons recommending that it should seek information about partner's honour holding in the trump suit. I call it the Poirot Grand Slam Force. Doubtless they will find some other name for it."

We were interrupted by the entry of his housekeeper.

"There's a young lady as wants a word with you, Monsieur Porret. She says her maternal uncle, the wealthy unmarried bachelor, Sir Guy Faversham, has been foully done to death, and Scotland Yard are baffled."

Having neatly unfolded the plot, she gave a meaningful sniff and ushered in the loveliest girl I had ever seen. She was perhaps two and twenty, with auburn hair and wonderful blue eyes, glistening with tears of sorrow.

"Sit down, I beg you, Mademoiselle. This is my associate, Captain Hastings. And you of course are Miss Emily Vavasour. No, do not derange yourself, it is not one of my celebrated deductions. Your distinguished visage has appeared many times in the society magazines."

"Only fifty-three," she murmured, blushing fetchingly. "Not counting last week's *Tatler*, which was so ghastly that I was completely unrecognisable. But here I am, prattling on about myself, not twelve hours after my poor uncle was found fatally murdered."

She dabbed her eyes with a tiny lace handkerchief, while I placed a consoling arm around her perfect shoulders.

"There there, my dear," I reassured her. "The Yard may be baffled but, with the aid of my friend Poirot, I will see that the murderer is brought to justice."

Poirot rose, preened his absurd waxed moustache, and puffed out his chest. "*Excusez moi*, but to humour an assistant most humble, would you kindly recount the details of Sir Guy's death?"

"I will try, Monsieur. Yesterday evening he invited three people to his Mayfair flat for dinner and bridge, and asked me to come and watch the play." She lowered her eyes modestly. "I am learning the game. Very slowly, I'm afraid."

"Really?" I asked. "Do you play Culbertson?"

"I try, Captain. Although his four no trump convention is somewhat beyond me. I have only just mastered simple Blackwood, which I use in nearly every auction."

"Do you? Then we must play a partnership some time."

"*Sacré!*" Poirot ejaculated. "Pray let us return to our muttons."

"Very well, Monsieur. After the first rubber, Borrocks, Uncle Guy's aged but faithful butler, informed him of an urgent telephone call. He excused himself, and I took his place. We played two rubbers, and I went to his study to tell him to come back quickly, as I had already lost fourteen shillings."

She broke off, overcome by grief. It was apparent that she could ill afford such a loss. Then, comforted by the manly pressure of my hand on hers, the plucky girl was able to continue. "He was slumped in the armchair by the telephone, with a fearful gash on his forehead. By his side was a heavy brass buddha, covered in blood, but, according to the handsome young man from Scotland Yard, no fingerprints. The wall safe was open, and his collection of flawless diamonds was missing."

"A motive!" I cried perspicaciously.

"I called the others," she continued. "Fortunately one of them was Doctor McTavish, the Harley Street obstetrician. He told us that Uncle Guy was dead, but, as far as he could tell, not pregnant. Then Major Ransome, the famous big game hunter, deeply tanned from his recent safari in Tanganyika, called the police."

Poirot nodded sagaciously. "I have four questions. First, did each player have occasion to quit the table while he was dummy?"

"Why yes, I believe so."

"Second, did the police fail to find the diamonds?"

"Yes, even after the most thorough search," she replied, colouring deeply.

"*Bien.* Third, yesterday it was very cold. Yet I suspect that the study window was wide open, *n'est-ce pas?*"

"*Oui* – I mean yes. But nobody could have climbed in. We were on the fourth floor."

"*Enfin*, there were three guests. Was the third a cool handsome lady, with the air of an adventuress?"

"How clever of you, Monsieur. Now I know how you solved the Orient Express mystery and caught the Hound of the Baskervilles. You have described Mrs Bravington exactly."

"It was dramatically inevitable. *Voyons!* Let us take a taxi to the *scène de crime*."

"We'll never get a taxi in this weather," I said, gazing out at the heavy sleet.

"To Poirot," he replied, "all things are possible."

Four hours later, the aged but faithful Borrocks admitted us to the flat. The police had left, leaving a trail of size twelve boot prints on the lavish Persian carpet.

"I haven't had a chance to clean up yet," Borrocks explained, "being so 'orribly shook up by the death of my late master." He wiped a tear from his cheek and I instantly removed him from my list of suspects.

Poirot went straight to the study and examined the safe.

"*Regardez*, Hastings. A Chubb, with an eight figure combination, which somehow the murderer must have discovered."

"But that is incredible," said Miss Vavasour. "*Mon oncle* changed it every day and confided it to no one."

"Then unless his memory was infallible, he must have recorded it somewhere."

He picked up a book from the table near the safe. "But what is this? *Ma tante sacrée!* It is a collection of bridge problems, with a book mark at page forty. And all the solutions have been torn out. But why? We must study the page in question."

♠ K
♡ AK
◊ AKQ
♣ A1098765

♠ AQJ
♡ QJ10
◊ J109876
♣ 2

Contract: 7NT. The ♠10 led.

I was still studying the problem when Miss Vavasour uttered a charming little sigh of resignation. "Bother!" she exclaimed. "I cannot reach my hand to enjoy the long diamonds. The suit is blocked."

"*Mais non*," said Poirot. "You simply overtake the ♠K, discard dummy's hearts on your spade winners and the top diamonds on your three hearts. Now you can run your winning diamonds and lead the club deuce to the ace for your thirteenth trick. Spectacular, but, for Poirot, not difficult."

"Even so, Monsieur, the jettison play never occurred to me. It was wonderful."

"Much more wonderful is the fact that I now know the combination. If we ignore the honour cards, and assume that the diamonds were led from the top, and the clubs discarded from the bottom, the sequence of cards played is 5-6-9-7-8-8-7-9."

He rapidly manipulated the dial and looked infuriatingly pleased with himself as the door flew open.

"*Voilà*! So our assassin has the ability to solve a bridge problem almost as quickly as Poirot. Mademoiselle, you have played with our three suspects. Which of them has such a skill?"

"I am afraid I'm not good enough to judge. They all seemed frightfully clever to me."

"*Tiens*! Then you must invite them back for another evening of bridge, *toute suite*. And Hastings and I will be kibitzers."

She paused uncertainly. "But will they accept?" she asked. "Surely they will see the invitation as melodramatic, bizarre, even tasteless."

"*Exactement*," Poirot replied. "So that when Hastings chronicles this adventure it will make a perfect final chapter."

Chapter Two

I prudently sipped the dry Martini which Miss Vavasour had so exquisitely prepared, and examined the guests at our bizarre, melodramatic and tasteless bridge party.

Major Ransome was well built, and damnably attractive, with his deep Tanganyika tan from a recent safari and the romantic scar above his right eyebrow, from an encounter with an unsporting rhino. His insolent gaze followed Miss Vavasour wherever she went, but I was pleased to see that she never returned his interest. The man was an out-and-out bounder, reputedly addicted to the Vienna bidding system, and, even worse, he addressed her as Emily.

Mrs Bravington bore a striking resemblance to Miss Marlene Dietrich. As she drank her sixth pink gin, she sat back, her striking figure stunningly revealed by a daring cocktail dress, as she studied us with an amused expression on her full crimson lips. A confirmed *femme fatale*, she was rumoured to be experimenting with multi-coloured two bids, thirty years before their time.

The tall, dour Hamish McTavish, who had delivered every royal baby since the Prince of Wales, seemed such an unlikely murderer that I suspected him immediately.

"I dinna approve this weird festivity so soon after Sir Guy's murder," he was telling Poirot. "But I mind you've a reputation for dramatic humbug, d'ye ken? So here I am. And I warn you that, if I'm a suspect, ye'll have the entire Hoose of Windsor doon on yer head."

Poirot bristled. References to his egg-shaped head invariably irked him. "Doctor," he said, "Poirot suspects everyone, even the butler."

"Borrocks!"

"I'm sorry you should think so," Poirot murmured, and turned sadly away.

Soon afterwards the players cut for partners and the first rubber began, with the ladies against the gentlemen.

I watched from my vantage point between the irascible Doctor and the alluring Mrs Bravington. She had the coolness to bring off an audacious crime, but could she solve tortuous bridge problems in a trice?

The very first hand provided a convincing answer.

Love All. Dealer South.

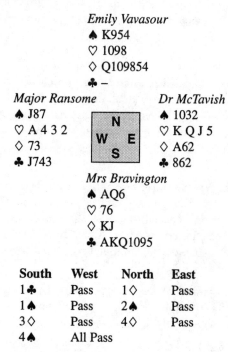

Emily Vavasour
♠ K954
♡ 1098
◇ Q109854
♣ —

Major Ransome
♠ J87
♡ A 4 3 2
◇ 73
♣ J743

Dr McTavish
♠ 1032
♡ K Q J 5
◇ A62
♣ 862

Mrs Bravington
♠ AQ6
♡ 76
◇ KJ
♣ AKQ1095

South	West	North	East
1♣	Pass	1◇	Pass
1♠	Pass	2♠	Pass
3◇	Pass	4◇	Pass
4♠	All Pass		

Mrs Bravington solved her rebid problem with a gentle one spade, having instructed her young partner that any change of suit was forcing. After a delicate auction, the adventuress reached four spades, the only game contract with any chance.

The defence began with three rounds of hearts, forcing declarer to ruff in hand. She cashed her top spades, and both defenders followed, leaving the following position:

Emily Vavasour
♠ K9
♡ –
◇ Q109854
♣ –

Major Ransome
♠ J
♡ 4
◇ 73
♣ J743

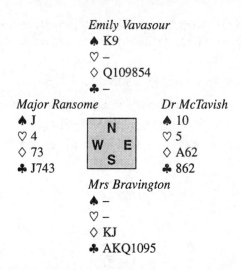

Dr McTavish
♠ 10
♡ 5
◇ A62
♣ 862

Mrs Bravington
♠ –
♡ –
◇ KJ
♣ AKQ1095

Now Mrs Bravington needed to establish diamonds and reach dummy to draw the outstanding trumps. From my viewpoint, it seemed impossible. If she led the ◇K, any defender with ace to three would hold up until the second round and then give partner a ruff. She would just have to hope that the ♣J fell.

Her solution, like her voluptuous figure, was breathtaking. She advanced the ◇J, overtaking with dummy's queen. The obstetrician was powerless. After going into protracted labour, he finally elected to duck. Now Mrs Bravington threw her ◇K on dummy's top trump, conceded a diamond and claimed.

"Should I have ducked?" McTavish asked.

"By all means," Ransome replied, "since ducking always gives an impression of expertise. But it would have made no difference if you had won. Whatever you returned, our charming opponent would have had no difficulty in reaching dummy to execute that same ingenious unblocking play."

"Why, thank you, Major," Mrs Bravington replied. "Compliments are especially welcome from the ranks of Tuscany."

Poor Miss Vavasour looked puzzled, clearly not following the classical allusion. I would of course explain it to her later, as soon as Poirot explained it to me.

At that moment, Borrocks, who had been patiently waiting to serve Mrs Bravington's tenth pink gin, leaned forward deferentially.

"Allow me to add my congratulations, madam," he whispered. "Your lead of the diamond knave was a real killer."

Seeing my look of astonishment, he approached me with a servile smirk. "Pay no attention, sir. I assure you my outburst was just a red 'erring, sir."

I was inclined to believe him, for I now regarded Mrs Bravington as our prime suspect.

Until the next rubber ....

Game All. Dealer West.

Emily Vavasour
♠ 432
♡ KQJ98
◇ 1072
♣ 42

Mrs Bravington
♠ A109765
♡ 104
◇ 8
♣ 9873

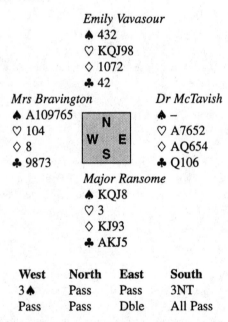

Dr McTavish
♠ –
♡ A7652
◇ AQ654
♣ Q106

Major Ransome
♠ KQJ8
♡ 3
◇ KJ93
♣ AKJ5

West	North	East	South
3♠	Pass	Pass	3NT
Pass	Pass	Dble	All Pass

Mrs Bravington's boldness in pre-empting with a far from solid six card suit was matched by Ransome's gambling three no trumps with no heart guard.

She led the ♠10, McTavish discarding the heart deuce. The Major won the trick, played his singleton heart and covered West's ten. McTavish ducked, won the heart continuation, on which the Major discarded his ♠8. McTavish now exited with a low club, apparently the least of three evils.

Ransome successfully finessed the ♣J, and cashed the ♣AK. At this point, I could not see for the life of me how he could get to dummy to enjoy the winning hearts, but with a devilish grin, and after a barely perceptible pause, he played the ◊9, overtaking with dummy's ten.

The doctor was forced to capture the trick, but now held only red cards. Whichever he led would create an entry to the table. The contract was, to use the current American expression, on ice.

"I've never known such luck," McTavish fumed.

"My dear doctor," Ransome drawled, "I had a perfect count of the hand. Of course you might have held the fourth club, but the false card of the queen, although automatic to an expert, would have outraged your code of Caledonian honesty. And to contrive an entry to dummy I needed Mrs Bravington's singleton diamond to be the eight. My nine was a routine unblock."

"I'm glad I was able to oblige you," Mrs Bravington said, with her Gioconda smile.

Whilst the players were agreeing the score, I remarked to Poirot that the two examples of excellent dummy play had a distinct similarity.

"Do you think Ransome and Mrs Bravington could be in collusion?" I whispered.

"*C'est possible*," he replied enigmatically. "There is also a similarity in their personalities, *n'est-ce pas?*"

"By jove, Poirot!" I exclaimed. "Does that mean you believe …?"

"Patience, *mon ami*." His eyes twinkled. "We have not quite reached the last chapter."

"You really are infuriating," I laughed affectionately. "I sometimes wonder how I resist the impulse to stangle you."

He thought for a moment. "Probably because without me you would never deduce the identity of the strangler."

The third rubber produced a lucky defence by Miss Vavasour.

Love All. Dealer South.

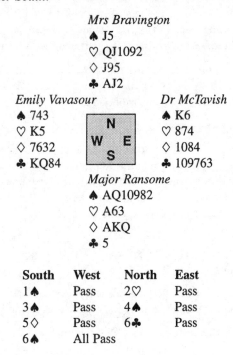

Mrs Bravington
♠ J5
♡ QJ1092
◇ J95
♣ AJ2

Emily Vavasour
♠ 743
♡ K5
◇ 7632
♣ KQ84

Dr McTavish
♠ K6
♡ 874
◇ 1084
♣ 109763

Major Ransome
♠ AQ10982
♡ A63
◇ AKQ
♣ 5

South	West	North	East
1♠	Pass	2♡	Pass
3♠	Pass	4♠	Pass
5◇	Pass	6♣	Pass
6♠	All Pass		

Ransome's characteristic selfishness in refusing to support his partner's hearts led me to reflect that when branding him a bounder I had been over-generous. The ♣K was led and taken in dummy. Ransome immediately ran the ♡Q. If this lost to the king he presumably planned to cross to dummy with a second heart and fall back on the spade finesse.

A cool assessment of the percentages followed by decisive action, I thought: ideal attributes for a ruthless killer. The fellow had guilt written over him.

Then, glancing at Miss Vavasour's hand, I suddenly realised that the poor lamb had sorted her cards wrongly. The ♡K was hidden amongst her diamonds. Now when her ♡5 appeared on the queen, declarer confidently repeated the finesse.

"Oh, my goodness!" Miss Vavasour gasped. "I've suddenly noticed I had the king all the time." Gathering the trick sheepishly, she tried to cash ♣Q and looked even more sheepish when it was ruffed. But Ransome could not reach the table for the trump finesse and the contract was doomed.

His look of chagrin was a joy to behold. A deep flush revealed a scar above his left eyebrow, probably from an encounter with an unsporting husband.

"What an incredible fluke, Emily," he complained.

"I'm terribly sorry," she said. "Would it have made any difference if I'd taken the first heart?"

"Don't let it worry you, my dear," said Mrs Bravington drily. "Even Napoleon made lucky mistakes. And on this occasion God was on the side of the small battalions."

An ingenious defensive alliance confirmed my theory that Ransome and Mrs Bravington would make a formidable pair of criminal accomplices. Never had I seen such perfectly synchronised duplicity.

North/South Game. Dealer West

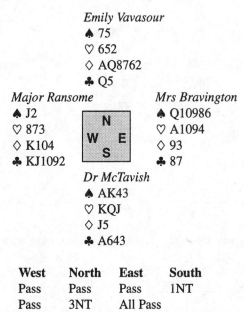

Emily Vavasour
♠ 75
♡ 652
◇ AQ8762
♣ Q5

Major Ransome
♠ J2
♡ 873
◇ K104
♣ KJ1092

Mrs Bravington
♠ Q10986
♡ A1094
◇ 93
♣ 87

Dr McTavish
♠ AK43
♡ KQJ
◇ J5
♣ A643

West	North	East	South
Pass	Pass	Pass	1NT
Pass	3NT	All Pass	

Miss Vavasour's diamonds persuaded the brave girl to raise the Doctor's vulnerable no trump opening to game. Ransome led the ♣J to the Q, 8 and 3. Declarer called for a small diamond on which Mrs Bravington played a mildly deceptive ◇3. At this point, neither defender could see any chance of defeating the contract in the normal course of events. Abnormality was clearly called for, so on declarer's ◇J Ransome craftily dropped the ten.

McTavish diagnosed an acute case of a guarded ◇K on his right, and prepared for an end play by first getting a count of the hand. A trained scientific observer, suit counting and reading defensive signals were his great strengths, but to the two adventurers his great weakness.

So on his ♡K they gave false counts with the ♡8 and ♡4. The ♡Q followed, to Ransome's ♡3 and Mrs Bravington's ♡A. When the ♣7 fell from her jewelled fingers, McTavish, reading her for for a 5-3-3-2 distribution, rose with his ♣A and cashed his third heart. He then played his ♠AK and, with a masterful air, a small spade.

This was the position he envisaged:

Emily Vavasour
♠ –
♡ –
◇ AQ876
♣ –

Major Ransome
♠ –
♡ 10
◇ 4
♣ K109

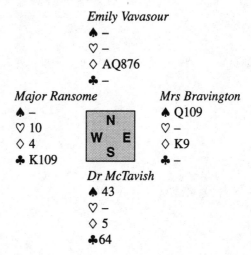

Mrs Bravington
♠ Q109
♡ –
◇ K9
♣ –

Dr McTavish
♠ 43
♡ –
◇ 5
♣64

As Poirot explained to me later, the Doctor was convinced that East would make only three more winners before being compelled to lead up to dummy's ◇AQ. But Mrs Bravington, exchanging a knowing smile with her caddish partner, cashed three spades and one heart.

"It's a bit of a cheek to give you medical advice, old man," Ransome told the apoplectic doctor. "But you really should watch your adrenalin secretions."

"It's a doonright ootrage," McTavish exploded. "Have the pair of you no conception of honest Christian signalling?"

"I can't speak for my partner," Ransome smirked, "but as an obstetrician you'll be sorry to know that conception is something I always try to avoid."

I felt an overwhelming compulsion to horsewhip the swine. How could he say such unmentionable things in front of a sweet young girl like Miss Vavasour? And Mrs Bravington's laughter showed that she was no better.

To a pair who could behave as badly as this, murder would be a minor indiscretion.

When the rubber eventually finished and Borrocks served refreshments, I took Poirot aside.

"Well Poirot? Have you solved the case?"

"Of course," he replied smugly. "Have you?"

Chapter Three

The little Belgian was in his element. The suspects were gathered, the atmosphere was electric, the floor was his.

"We are met," he announced, "in the very flat where Sir Guy Faversham was murdered. Scotland Yard are baffled, but fortunately his charming niece had the perspicacity to consult Hercule Poirot."

Mrs Bravington smiled at his conceit, McTavish snorted and Ransome guffawed loudly.

"You may laugh, Major," said Poirot. "To you I am the comical foreigner, whose speech is full of quaint Gallic phrases, but I tell you, *sacré bleu*, that this is a trick to put criminals off their guard."

"And which of us have you put off guard?" asked Mrs Bravington, archly.

"Patience, Madame. I will be brief," he told her, and I silently prayed that for once he really meant it.

"Our first mystery," Poirot continued, "was the disappearance of the stolen diamonds. And the solution was so simple that any fool could have seen it."

"And did you?" asked Ransome.

"*Naturellement*," replied Poirot, whose long experience of my sharp wit had inured him to such feeble sallies. "Why was the study window open on such a cold night? Because the diamonds had been thrown out to an accomplice, probably the accomplice who had telephoned Sir Guy to lure him to his death."

"Monsieur, that is absolutely brilliant," said Miss Vavasour, her eyes shining with admiration.

"*Merci*, Mademoiselle. The second mystery was how the secret combination of the safe was discovered. But I proved it was deciphered from a book of advanced bridge problems, so the murderer must be a player of expert rank. This, *mes amis*, was the reason for tonight's party."

"Hoots, man!" cried McTavish. "Will ye nae get on wi'it? I've two pairs of twins to deliver before the night's oot."

"Then you may go, Doctor. After watching you play, I have eliminated you from all suspicion."

The doctor leaped slowly to his feet. "What are you drivelling about, man? I didna play a wrong card all evening."

"You think not? Then let us analyse the second hand of the opening rubber."

East/West Game. Dealer West.

Major Ransome
♠ 98
♡ A986
◇ J108
♣ AQ102

Mrs Bravington
♠ AJ7
♡ KQ1053
◇ K
♣ K975

```
        N
    W       E
        S
```

Emily Vavasour
♠ K6543
♡ 742
◇ 32
♣ 843

Dr McTavish
♠ Q102
♡ J
◇ AQ97654
♣ J6

West	North	East	South
1♡	Pass	Pass	2◇
Double	3NT	Pass	4◇
Pass	5◇	All Pass	

"You will recall, Doctor, that the opening lead was the heart king, won in dummy."

"Aye, and it was clear as daylight I needed both minor suit finesses. But I lost the second trick to Mrs Bravington's bare ◇ K, and when she switched to spades I was done for."

"Exactly. So permit me to give you a lesson in bridge logic, most elementary. One, if Mrs Bravington, a redoubtable defender, held the two top spades, she would assuredly have led one. Two, since she did not do so, her partner must have one. Three, since Miss Vavasour had passed the opening bid, she could not also hold a minor suit king. Conclusion: your only hope was to lay down your ◇ A and pray for the king to be single. As indeed it was."

McTavish was not convinced. "Verra far-fetched," he said.

Poirot's shrug was eloquent. "Of course Doctor, if you would rather be considered a murder suspect than a poor bridge player, there is nothing more to be said. Nevertheless, I have crossed you off my list."

"And who does that leave?" Mrs Bravington enquired.

Poirot gave a little bow. "To begin with, both you and Major Ransome are players of the front rank."

"So it was one of us?" Ransome grinned. "I can't wait to find out which."

"Then let us suppose it was you, Major. If you left the table while you were dummy, you might have had only two minutes to enter the study, kill Sir Guy, locate the bridge book, solve the problem, decode the solution, open the safe, steal the diamonds, open the window, throw out the diamonds and stroll back here as if nothing had happened."

"He would be *très fatigué*," Mrs Bravington remarked.

"It is utterly impossible, Madame. To accomplish everything would require three visits. Let us suppose that the first accounted for the murder and the disposal of the incriminating fingerprints. Can you imagine the killer returning to the bridge table and calmly awaiting the next opportunity to be dummy? A half hour might pass without partner making a bid. And at any moment the faithful Borrocks might discover his master's body. Our two bridge masters showed this evening that they were bold, but not reckless."

"But, Poirot ... " I began.

"Ah yes," he silenced me. "My friend Hastings has suggested that they could be accomplices, but even so, the same time pressures would operate, albeit to a lesser extent."

"But Monsieur." Miss Vavasour said. "Does this mean you have failed?"

"It means that the murderer had the opportunity to discover the combination before the bridge party began."

"Borrocks!"

The faithful butler, who had been lurking in a dark corner, uttered a groan of protest. "It wasn't me, sir. I could never have lifted that 'eavy brass buddha, not with my arthritis, I couldn't."

"I agree, Borrocks," Poirot said kindly, and turned gravely to Miss Vavasour.

"You made three mistakes, Mademoiselle. When I described the solution to the single dummy problem, you called it a jettison play. *Tiens!* This is 1935. As yet, the term is familiar only to a small group of experts. Your other errors were your pair of 'accidental' defensive brilliancies. One would have been acceptable. Two defied belief. Your baring the king of hearts to frustrate Major Ransome was ingenious. But one of your later deceptions was diabolically clever. You will recall the hand."

Game All. Dealer South.

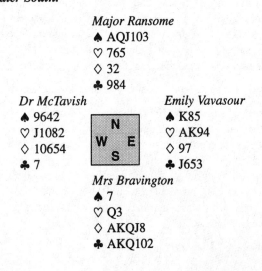

Major Ransome
♠ AQJ103
♡ 765
◇ 32
♣ 984

Dr McTavish
♠ 9642
♡ J1082
◇ 10654
♣ 7

Emily Vavasour
♠ K85
♡ AK94
◇ 97
♣ J653

Mrs Bravington
♠ 7
♡ Q3
◇ AKQJ8
♣ AKQ102

South	West	North	East
2♦	Pass	2♠	Pass
3♣	Pass	3♠	Pass
4♣	Pass	5♣	All Pass

"After Mrs Bravington had shown a powerful two-suiter, she finished in what appeared to be a straightforward club game. A heart was led, and Miss Vavasour paused nervously after cashing her ♡ AK. She pulled out a small heart, and pushed it back again. She repeated the pantomime with a small diamond. She radiated maidenly indecision. Finally, she produced the ♠5!"

Poirot regarded Miss Vavasour with reluctant admiration. "Your bemused expression, when it apparently dawned on you that to lead into dummy's tenace was the action of an imbecile, was a masterpiece. Mrs Bravington took the trick with dummy's ten and played two rounds of trumps. On discovering the bad break she had no way of reaching the table to take the club finesse."

"I see it all," said Mrs Bravington. "Had she played that spade with an air of purpose I would have suspected her motive and finessed trumps immediately."

"Exactly," Poirot agreed. "She is a true *artiste*."

Miss Vavasour squared her perfect shoulders and defiantly faced her accuser. "Then why did I risk everything? I could have simply let through the contracts".

"Not at a shilling a hundred. I sensed your rapacity when we first met, and you were deranged more by the loss of fourteen shillings than by the loss of your uncle."

"Really? Then why would a guilty person call in the world's greatest detective?"

"Because you knew that when Scotland Yard is baffled they always send for Poirot. It was a daring pre-emptive bid."

She chuckled confidently. "But how could a sweet little thing like me have wielded that heavy brass buddha?"

"Mademoiselle, today I telephoned the headmistress of your old school. You were captain of hockey, lacrosse, netball and swimming. And of ju-jitsu, until you had broken the arms of half the sixth form and three mathematics teachers."

I was unable to believe my ears. Poirot, for the first time in his life, had cheated our readers, introducing last minute evidence hitherto concealed from them. But worse was to come!

"There is worse to come," he said. "Since there are no public telephones in Mayfair I deduced that your accomplice must reside nearby, and my friend Inspector Japp discovered that one of the flats opposite was occupied by your old school friend, Fiona Cholmondley."

I was stunned. I could not let my friend continue in an error of such magnitude. "Poirot!" I remonstrated. "It is pronounced Chumley."

"However she is pronounced, Hastings, she is a suspect most prime."

At that moment Borrocks, who had slipped quietly away on finding he was not a suspect, returned, announcing that there was a telephone call for Poirot, who lifted the receiver and listened for a minute.

"*Merci*, Inspector," he said. He replaced the receiver, and faced Miss Vavasour with an expression of triumph.

"Mademoiselle, would it surprise you to know that your friend has been apprehended while in possession of the diamonds, and has confessed everything?"

"The little fool!" she hissed. Then she recovered herself and smiled at Poirot. "But you too made a mistake, Monsieur. My sending for you was not a pre-emptive bid. I wanted to defeat the great Hercule Poirot." Her voice was steady, her lovely head held high. "And I would have done, but for that pathetic Fiona. By now she and the diamonds should have been miles away."

"They probably are, Mademoiselle."

"But you said ..."

"I merely enquired whether a certain hypothesis would surprise you. Apparently it did."

She stared at him, her eyes blazing. It stuck me that she could scarcely have provided a more perfect climax.

I was wrong! Suddenly she drew from her evening bag a small, pearl-handled revolver.

Poirot turned white. Normally guns held no terror for him, but this one was pointed at his moustache!

"Don't try and stop me." she cried, and fled into the study. There was the sound of a key turning in the lock.

It took Mrs Bravington nearly a minute to break down the door, and when we burst into the room there was no sign of Miss Vavasour, but the window was open. We looked out, expecting to see a broken body on the pavement below, but there was nothing.

"Look!" Ransome exclaimed. Driving off into the night was a large furniture van. Did I fancy seeing a small, lovely figure crouching on its roof?

"No, Hastings," said Poirot gently. "It was not fancy. I saw her too. The van must have been pre-arranged. She would never have jumped otherwise. It is not in her nature to make vulnerable sacrifices."

"But, Poirot, are you going to let her escape?"

"No, I shall inform the good Japp immediately. But I doubt if he will catch her. She will make a new life somewhere, and then, after skilful cosmetic surgery, pursue a career suitable to her fiendish gifts, probably as a bridge professional. In a few years time she will certainly be playing for the British Ladies."

Mrs Bravington looked thoughtful. "I wonder if she'll need a partner?" she murmured.

"Poirot," I said firmly. "Tonight you proved your case with evidence not previously known to the rest of us. How on earth can I publish this story?"

"Do not derange yourself, *mon vieux*. This episode will be read only by bridge experts. They will guess the solution anyway."

THE CLUB

2
THE CLUB

Chapter One

Oliver Lombard read Michael McDeal's résumé for the twelfth time. The man was perfect. A Life Master at seventeen. The Spingold at twenty-one. And last year the World Junior Championship. Even better, he was a high school drop out, drank like a fish, smoked like a furnace and screwed like a rabbit. The guy was a born bridge pro.

There was a knock on the door. Lombard opened it, smiled broadly at the good-looking young man and shook his hand firmly.

"You must be Michael McDeal."

"Yes. But please call me Mick."

"For a moment I thought you were Tom Cruise."

"It happens, sir. Tom has the same problem in reverse."

Mick was slim and athletic. While his contemporaries had been destroying their bodies playing football, years of strenuous shuffling and dealing had toned his muscles to perfection. He relaxed confidently in an Eames chair and surveyed the opulent 40 by 40 office. Like the rest of the exclusive Lucifer Club, it shrieked big money.

Lombard was opening a bottle of champagne. "I've been admiring some of your plays," he said. "Particularly this one. Perhaps you'd talk me through it."

He gave Mick a printed copy of a hand.

Game All. Dealer South.

$\spadesuit$ 642
$\heartsuit$ 1095
$\diamond$ K9753
$\clubsuit$ J4

```
      N
   W     E
      S
```

$\spadesuit$ AK10
$\heartsuit$ AK3
$\diamond$ Q842
$\clubsuit$ A107

South	West	North	East
2NT	Pass	3$\clubsuit$(i)	Pass
3$\diamond$(ii)	Pass	3NT	All Pass

(i)   5 card Stayman
(ii) Denying a 5 card major

"Okay," said Mick, "West was a solid player, long on experience, short on flair. He led the $\spadesuit$3, East played the $\spadesuit$Q. I took with my $\spadesuit$K, and everything depended on how I handled the diamonds."

Lombard looked impatient. "I realise that, Mick. What I don't get is why you started with the $\diamond$Q. Surely the percentage play is low toward the king? West might hold the $\diamond$A single."

Mick's lips formed the familiar curl of the bridge expert being asked to explain the obvious to a palooka. "West wasn't likely to hold a singleton diamond unless he had specifically a 4-4-1-4 distribution. In which case his lead from jack empty would seem a pretty dumb choice with two other four-card suits to choose from. So I read him for 4-4-3-2 or 4-3-3-3. Are you with me?"

"Just about."

"Well, as I expected, the guy covered my queen with the $\diamond$A. Then he tried to put me under pressure by returning the $\diamond$6."

"But he didn't succeed?"

"No, I could read him like a book. Besides, East dropped the ◊ 10, so it was a restricted choice situation. I let it run round to my ◊ 8. You know the full layout."

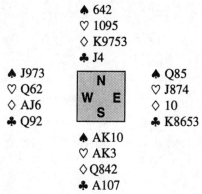

```
                    ♠ 642
                    ♡ 1095
                    ◊ K9753
                    ♣ J4
    ♠ J973         N            ♠ Q85
    ♡ Q62      W       E        ♡ J874
    ◊ AJ6          S            ◊ 10
    ♣ Q92                       ♣ K8653
                    ♠ AK10
                    ♡ AK3
                    ◊ Q842
                    ♣ A107
```

Lombard smiled his appreciation.

"The other declarer started with a low diamond from hand and, when West played low, he went up with dummy's queen. And he was a famous player, Mick."

"He's been famous for half a century. That's his problem."

Lombard smiled with the satisfaction of a man still in his early forties. "Well, Mick, a card reader like you doesn't need to be told why I asked you here."

"You want me to join your team."

"Yes, and to act as bridge host at the Club."

"What does that involve, sir?"

"Please call me Mr Lombard. We have five bridge professionals. You'll make six. You'll spend around half your time playing rubber bridge."

"How high are the stakes?"

"Five dollars."

"A hundred?"

"A point. I've seen $20,000 won and lost on a single rubber. High rollers come here from all over the world. Tycoons, movie stars, senators, royalty. Even Presidents."

"And most of them lose?"

"Enough. When the lamb goes to the slaughter, he might eat the butcher, Mick, but we always bet on the butcher. A young tiger like you should win at least five thousand a day. Split right down the middle."

Mick's mind raced like a demented cash register. "That's generous," he said, his voice thick with greed.

"I know." Lombard poured two glasses. "That's probably why nobody ever leaves the club."

"Nobody?"

"Our staff turnover is an absolute zero. Naturally we expect a lot in return. You'll put in a sixty-hour week. When you're not playing rubbers you'll be polishing your techniques with the other pros."

"Who are they?"

"Steinway, Miller, Gorman, Bidwell and O'Shea."

Mick was impressed. "I wondered why I hadn't seen much of them lately. I thought they'd sort of dropped out."

Lombard laughed and said, "No they sort of dropped in, and decided to stay."

Mick sipped his champagne. It wasn't domestic. "What makes you think my technique needs polishing?"

"Good question. Here's another of your efforts, one from the Spring Nationals."

He produced another printed deal which Mick, with the true humility of a World Junior Champion, instantly recollected as an example of unimaginative defence. By his partner of course.

Love All. Dealer South.

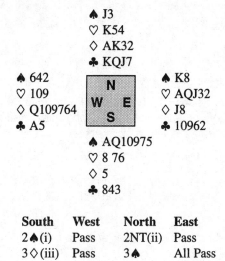

                    ♠ J3
                    ♡ K54
                    ◇ AK32
                    ♣ KQJ7

    ♠ 642   ♠ K8
    ♡ 109   ♡ AQJ32
    ◇ Q109764   ◇ J8
    ♣ A5   ♣ 10962

                    ♠ AQ10975
                    ♡ 8 76
                    ◇ 5
                    ♣ 843

South	West	North	East
2♠(i)	Pass	2NT(ii)	Pass
3◇(iii)	Pass	3♠	All Pass

(i)   Weak
(ii) General enquiry
(iii) Poor hand, good suit

"Your team-mate played in three spades. The ♡10 was led, and held the trick. West was a class act. He could see four defensive tricks, three hearts and the ace of clubs. He needed one more. So instead of continuing with a routine ♡9, he laid down the ♣A. Now he switched back to hearts and was able to discard a club on the third round. A club ruff was the setting trick."

"I remember the hand, Mr Lombard. But, when I sat east in the other room, my partner wasn't up to cashing the ♣A. He continued hearts and the contract was cold."

"You weren't so hot yourself, Mr McDeal. You should have overtaken the first trick with the ♡J and returned a club. Now, when you came in with the second heart, you could have achieved the same result."

"Yes, but … "

"Let's face it, Mick. You didn't find the right line."

"Nobody's perfect." Mick was annoyed. "Would you have found it?"

"Hell no, I'm just a competent player. But I've got some of the best hired help in the country. Steinway and the others spotted it in a flash. Yes, I know you've just won the World Juniors. But are you ready for the grown-up version?"

Mick grinned and said, "Okay, so my technique needs polishing. But what's in it for you, Mr Lombard?"

"Call me Oliver. Personal pride, prestige for the club. My team has been training for two years. Soon we'll take on the world. And I want you with us, Mick."

"How about fringe benefits?"

"You're drinking one of them. You'll have a BMW and an Armani wardrobe. You'll be playing with multi-millionaires, so you've got to look like one."

He leaned forward. "And before you're thirty, I'll lay odds you'll be one."

"It sounds good, Oliver."

"Make it Ollie. One more point. When a guest loses at bridge, he sometimes tries to win it back at blackjack or roulette. We'd like you to kind of encourage him."

"How do I do that, Ollie?"

"You might tell him about the other suck– I mean players who've made good their losses in five minutes."

Mick glared at him. "I'm a bridge pro, Ollie. Not a damned pimp."

"Tout Mick, tout. Pimp comes later. And you get ten per cent of their losses."

Mick shook his head. Did Lombard really think he could bribe one of the game's most ethical players? And suppose a mark lost ten grand or so. Ten per cent of that was only ....

"When do I start, Ollie?"

Chapter Two

At 1.40pm on the following Monday, Lombard made up a table with Mick against two oil-rich sheikhs who insisted on playing as partners. They needed to be rich. Mick had just made a spectacular grand slam and his arrogant expression suggested he was about to clinch the rubber.

Game All. Dealer East.

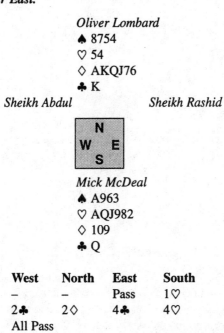

Oliver Lombard
♠ 8754
♡ 54
♦ AKQJ76
♣ K

Sheikh Abdul   *Sheikh Rashid*

Mick McDeal
♠ A963
♡ AQJ982
♦ 109
♣ Q

West	North	East	South
–	–	Pass	1♡
2♣	2♦	4♣	4♡
All Pass			

Sheikh Abdul promptly led the ♠Q, on which Rashid played the ♠K. Mick reviewed his options without enthusiasm. The obvious line was to win the trick, cross to the table with a diamond and take the trump finesse. If it succeeded, he wouldn't be able to get back to dummy without using up his diamond entry, so he would be forced to lay down his ♡A, hoping East's ♡K was a doubleton.

Having dismissed this possibility as distinctly remote, he started to figure West's probable distribution. He needed six clubs for his vulnerable overcall, and must hold four spades, since East's ♠K must surely be a singleton. And if Abdul had held a singleton diamond he probably would have led it, so his likely distribution was 4-1-2-6. This meant that Mick could make his contract only if West's singleton heart was the king. So, with more hope than conviction, he laid down the ♡A at trick two.

Sheikh Abdul produced the ♡K with an expression of superstitious awe, and Mick claimed his thirteen tricks.

The complete deal was:

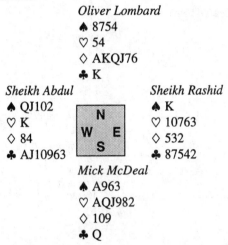

Oliver Lombard
♠ 8754
♡ 54
◇ AKQJ76
♣ K

Sheikh Abdul
♠ QJ102
♡ K
◇ 84
♣ AJ10963

Sheikh Rashid
♠ K
♡ 10763
◇ 532
♣ 87542

Mick McDeal
♠ A963
♡ AQJ982
◇ 109
♣ Q

Mick had an uneasy feeling that he had seen this hand before. He made a mental note to find out what *déjà vu* meant.

In answer to Abdul's polite enquiry, Mick briefly explained his reasoning and offered a sycophantic addition. "Another indication, gentlemen, was the admirable precision of your bidding methods. If your partner had held four hearts to the king in addition to his spade honour, he might have made an unassuming cue bid, rather than a pre-emptive raise in clubs."

"True," agreed Sheikh Rashid unassumingly.

Sheikh Abdul bowed eloquently. "Congratulations, my young friend. It is an honour to lose to a player of such consummate skill."

Mick knew no Arabic but he made a mental note to look up 'consummate'.

"Thank you, Sheikh," he said. "I expect you'll win it all back in five minutes at the roulette wheel," he added with well-bred delicacy.

"What a splendid idea. Possibly our luck will change." Abdul regarded Lombard with an oil-rich smile. "And then, perhaps ... the eighteenth floor."

Mick looked puzzled. "But this is only a seventeen-floor building."

"You must make allowances for Mick," Lombard said. "He isn't used to counting beyond thirteen."

When the sheikhs had left, Lombard gave Mick a nod of approval and said, "How about a champagne lunch in my office?"

"Your office?"

"That's where I keep the Dom Perignon. Can't you tell the difference?"

Mick made a mental note to learn the difference. Ten minutes later he was demolishing a lobster salad and admiring four portraits behind Lombard's 10 by 8 desk.

"Do you recognise them?" Lombard asked.

"They seem familiar."

"Goldblatt, Al Smith, McTaggart and Rose Jones. They were four great bridge players."

Mick noticed the change of tense. "Were, Ollie?"

Lombard looked suitably sad. "They all worked here." he sighed, "But Harry Goldblatt got drunk and fell off the roof of this building."

Mick winced. "That's some fall."

"The fall was no problem," Lombard said, with genuine sorrow. "It was the landing that killed him. It was just after Al drove his BMW into a cement mixer."

Mick felt sick. "And McTaggart?"

"He was fatally struck by a golf ball. It was unbelievable."

"It happens, Ollie."

"At a baseball game? And Rose was the saddest of all. She blew her brains out."

"That's terrible."

"It was." Lombard wiped away a tear. "But at least she had the decency not to do it at the Club."

"But four deaths. All violent, all bridge players, That's one hell of a coincidence, Ollie."

Lombard considered this as though it had never occurred to him. "I guess it is at that. But don't worry, Mick. Have some more lobster. I had it flown in from Maine."

He filled Mick's glass with champagne. "And stop frowning." His smile reminded Mick of an avuncular crocodile. "I'm sure nothing violent will happen to you. I'd hate to see *your* picture hanging on my office wall."

Chapter Three

Art Steinway was the maverick of the team, a fine player, but a difficult partner. He was tall and skinny, with angular features and a permanently cynical expression.

He was the fastest player Mick had ever seen, with a genius for persuading his opponents to play badly. Thankfully, Mick was his partner.

Love All. Dealer East.

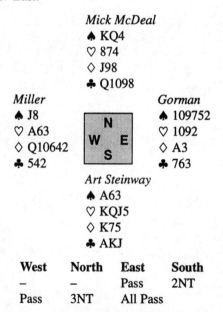

                    Mick McDeal
                    ♠ KQ4
                    ♡ 874
                    ◊ J98
                    ♣ Q1098

    Miller   *Gorman*
    ♠ J8   ♠ 109752
    ♡ A63   N   ♡ 1092
    ◊ Q10642   W   E   ◊ A3
    ♣ 542   S   ♣ 763

                    Art Steinway
                    ♠ A63
                    ♡ KQJ5
                    ◊ K75
                    ♣ AKJ

West	North	East	South
–	–	Pass	2NT
Pass	3NT	All Pass	

After an uninformative auction, Miller began with an orthodox ◊ 4. Gorman played the ◊ A, and Art Steinway smoothly dropped the ◊ K.

Gorman was a studious type. He regarded this card through his designer horn-rims, and placing declarer with king-queen and another diamond, switched eruditely to the ♡10, hoping to find Miller with ♡AQJx, Steinway covered with the ♡K and Miller looked sour, but there was nothing he could do to stop declarer making ten tricks.

"A diamond return beats it," he grunted.

"I know that now," said Gorman. "But it's charming of you to point it out to me."

"I'd have defended the same way," said Mick. "Dropping the diamond king was godlike." He wanted to keep in with Steinway, and knew that *godlike* was his favourite form of self-description.

"It was routine," Steinway drawled. "Stick around long enough and plays like that will be second nature." He studied Mick for a few seconds. "Or in your case maybe third."

"He'll stick around long enough," Miller said. He was the team captain, a short stocky guy in his forties, who took his position very seriously. "Nobody leaves the Club."

"Except Goldblatt," Steinway giggled. "He left via the roof."

"He'd been drinking too much." Miller frowned critically at Steinway's glass. "Like you, Art."

"I often wonder what poor Harry was doing on the roof," Steinway said, defiantly pouring himself another Jim Beam. "Perhaps he was looking for floor eighteen."

Miller glared at him. "Nobody's allowed on floor eighteen. Except special guests."

"And special hostesses, Miller. Don't forget the special hostesses."

"That's none of your business, Steinway. And it's your deal."

"I agree," Gorman said. "Talk like that could get back to the Slasher, Steinway. And he might trade you in for a Bechstein."

Mick had never heard of Bechstein. He made a mental note to look him up in the master points list. But he had met the Slasher once. He was Lombard's security chief, a big, mean, hard-eyed man who he didn't want to meet twice.

The next hand was dealt, and Gorman was tested with another defensive problem, as Steinway once again demonstrated his flair for projecting illusions.

North/South Game. Dealer South.

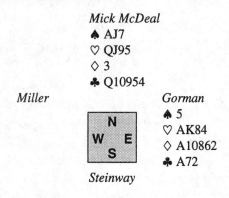

Mick McDeal
♠ AJ7
♡ QJ95
◇ 3
♣ Q10954

Miller

Gorman
♠ 5
♡ AK84
◇ A10862
♣ A72

Steinway

South	West	North	East
1♠	Pass	1NT(i)	Double
2♠	Pass	4♠(ii)	All Pass

(i) Forcing, intending to bid 3♠ next round
(ii) Probably justified when partner has shown 6 or more

Miller led the ♡2. From Gorman's point of view this could have been third or fourth best. He took dummy's ♡Q with the ♡K, and marked time by playing ace and another diamond, on which declarer played the ◇5 and ◇K, and Miller petered with the ◇9 and ◇4. Steinway advanced the ♠Q, which held, and a small spade to dummy's ♠J. West followed with the ♠4 and ♠6, and Steinway continued with a low club from the table.

Gorman rose with his ♣A and when the ♣K appeared on his left, and partner contributed the ♣8. He pointed his intellectual nose at the ceiling. If the ♡A was not standing up, where else could the setting trick come from? He tried to visualise a layout which could account for the play so far.

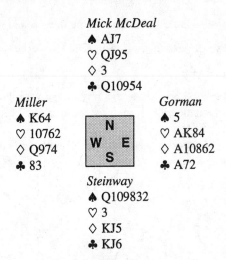

Mick McDeal
♠ AJ7
♡ QJ95
◇ 3
♣ Q10954

Miller
♠ K64
♡ 10762
◇ Q974
♣ 83

Gorman
♠ 5
♡ AK84
◇ A10862
♣ A72

Steinway
♠ Q109832
♡ 3
◇ KJ5
♣ KJ6

Pleased with his analysis, he led a low diamond, hoping that his partner's ◇ Q would force dummy and promote his lone ♠ K for the setting trick.

But the actual deal had been rather different:

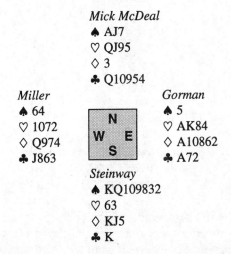

Mick McDeal
♠ AJ7
♡ QJ95
◇ 3
♣ Q10954

Miller
♠ 64
♡ 1072
◇ Q974
♣ J863

Gorman
♠ 5
♡ AK84
◇ A10862
♣ A72

Steinway
♠ KQ109832
♡ 63
◇ KJ5
♣ K

With a wolfish grin, Steinway ruffed the ◇ Q in dummy and shed his heart loser on the established ♣ Q to make his impossible game.

Miller was not impressed. "What's got into you today, partner? If I hold king third of trumps, I think I'm capable of communicating the fact with a trump peter."

"Really? Then you should have told me you'd improved so much."

"Very true, old sport," Steinway agreed. "But I think the expression you're looking for is 'Well played, Art!'"

Mick reflected that he was going to enjoy bridge with the pros. And that eighteenth floor sounded like somewhere he'd like to be.

In the next rubber, Mick had a chance to achieve the extremely difficult feat of impressing Steinway.

Game All. Dealer South.

Gorman
♠ 9754
♡ AKQJ
◊ A63
♣ QJ

Miller   Mick McDeal

Steinway
♠ AQJ
♡ 632
◊ J754
♣ AK7

South	West	North	East
1NT	Pass	2♣	Pass
2◊	Pass	6NT	All Pass

Miller led the ♣10 after Gorman had propelled Steinway into a dubious no trump slam. Steinway took in dummy and played a spade to the queen, which held. Superficially, he would need king to three spades onside to make the contract, but there were some squeeze chances. He crossed to a heart and led a diamond from the table. Mick rose with the ◊Q and exited passively with a heart. Steinway repeated the spade finesse and cashed his club and heart winners. On the last heart, Mick, who so far had followed suit, discarded the ◊10, leaving Art to study the three-card ending:

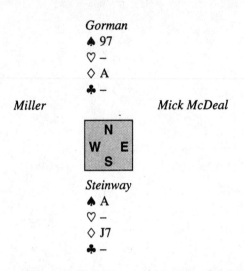

Gorman
♠ 97
♡ –
◊ A
♣ –

Miller   *Mick McDeal*

Steinway
♠ A
♡ –
◊ J7
♣ –

From declarer's point of view, Mick had clearly started with the ♠K and, judging from his early play, the ◊KQ. This would leave him with two possible holdings:

♠ Kx	or	♠ K
♡ –		♡ –
◊ K		◊ Kx
♣ –		♣ –

Steinway, like any genuine master, elected to play for the first alternative, as he had not brought off a criss-cross squeeze for several weeks. When he cashed dummy's ◊A and the ◊K did not drop, he shrugged philosophically.

"So the spades were 3-3 all along," he said.

"Of course," Mick replied, revealing his remaining cards with a yawn, while memorising the deal for his scrapbook.

Gorman
♠ 9754
♡ AKQJ
◇ A63
♣ QJ

Miller
♠ 1063
♡ 1094
◇ K92
♣ 10984

```
       N
    W     E
       S
```

Mick McDeal
♠ K82
♡ 875
◇ Q108
♣ 6532

Steinway
♠ AQJ
♡ 632
◇ J754
♣ AK7

Steinway regarded Mick with reluctant respect. "Welcome to the Club, McDeal," he said. "Your defence was …." He paused to select the adjective which would most perfectly reflect the esteem in which he held his new colleague.

"Godlike?" Mick suggested.

"Adequate," Steinway amended.

Chapter Four

At 10.00pm on Friday, Mick left the Club early to visit his favourite singles bar. He was halfway through his second Harvey Wallbanger with a Bacardi chaser when a girl glided to his table like a limousine on a runway.

"You're Mick McDeal, aren't you?"

She was blonde, with long slim legs, beautiful eyes and a seductive smile. Mick was sure he was about to be propositioned and started to rehearse his acceptance speech.

"And who are you?" he asked.

She whipped out a badge from the top of a black silk stocking. "Jane Florence, FBI Special Agent."

Mick was thrilled. He had never had an FBI agent before. "Have a seat," he leered.

"Why not?" She sat down close to him. He felt weak.

"You're Lucifer's new bridge pro, aren't you?" she asked.

"How do you know?"

"We watch that place like hawks."

"Why?"

"Because the Bureau doesn't employ doves. I've been sent here to warn you. You know about Goldblatt, Smith, McTaggart and Jones?"

"Of course. The four dead bridge stars."

"Well their deaths weren't accidental. They were wasted, Mick. Probably because they wanted to leave the Club. Nobody leaves the Club."

"I don't believe you."

"Then let me introduce you to someone you'll have to believe."

A short bald man got up from the next table and joined them. Mick knew him at once. He was hard-hitting, tough-talking, bullshitting, square-shooting Benton Boyles, Director of the FBI under six Presidents, possibly seven. Mick stood respectfully, but a large powerful hand pushed him down again.

"Keep a low profile, Mr McDeal," Boyles said. "We're just three lonely people in a singles bar, desperately seeking romance. Along with thirty more of my agents you can see around us."

Mick surveyed the bar. Every table was occupied by hard, lean men and women, all engaged in earnest conversation, but ready to flash into action at a sign from their chief. Boyles sat next to Mick, their legs touching.

Mick wished he was Jane Florence.

"Mr McDeal," Boyles said. "You're in deep shit, right up to your ankles. And you're standing on your head."

Mick gulped at his drink, while he analysed what Boyles had said with typical Life Master brilliance. "That sounds bad," he said finally.

"The Lucifer Club is owned by the Mob."

"The Mob?"

"The Syndicate, the Organisation, the Cosa Nostra. The cards are stacked, the dice are loaded, the wheels are fixed, the girls are whores, the waiters are pushers. Do you want me to go on?"

"Yes."

"Okay. The walls are wired, the beds are bugged, the drinks are spiked and the food is pure salmonella."

Mick froze. "Not the lobster!"

Boyles thought for a while. "No, not the lobster. It's flown in from Maine. But half the politicians in this country are being blackmailed by Oliver Lombard. He's nearly got the damned government in his hip pocket."

Mick decided to play it cool. "What has all this got to do with me?"

"This afternoon you gained a big penalty against a famous senator."

"You're well informed, Director."

"He wasn't a senator. He and his partner were undercover agents." Boyles presented Mick with a deal printed on FBI paper.

North/South Game. Dealer East.

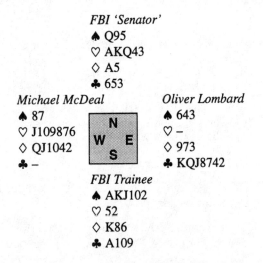

FBI 'Senator'
♠ Q95
♡ AKQ43
♢ A5
♣ 653

Michael McDeal
♠ 87
♡ J109876
♢ QJ1042
♣ –

Oliver Lombard
♠ 643
♡ –
♢ 973
♣ KQJ8742

FBI Trainee
♠ AKJ102
♡ 52
♢ K86
♣ A109

Mick recalled the auction, which contained a very strange bid by Lombard, followed by a gung-ho sequence from the two agents.

West	North	East	South
–	–	Pass!	1♠
Pass	2♡	Pass	2NT
Pass	3♠	Pass	4♣
Pass	4◊	Pass	5◊
Double	6♠	Double	All Pass

"Oliver Lombard dealt and passed," Boyle continued. "Didn't it strike you as crazy that at favourable vulnerability he didn't pre-empt?"

"Well it worked out well."

"Sure. After an uncontested auction, the good guys were bound to reach the spade slam. Then his Lightner double asked you to lead a heart for him to ruff, and of course you chose the ♡6, demanding a club return. When the smoke finally cleared, you wrote 1100 above the line. I know, because it depleted Bureau funds by eleven grand, a quarter of which is now yours."

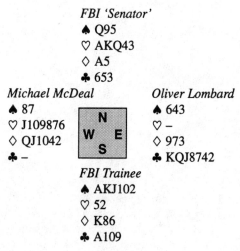

FBI 'Senator'
- ♠ Q95
- ♡ AKQ43
- ◊ A5
- ♣ 653

Michael McDeal
- ♠ 87
- ♡ J109876
- ◊ QJ1042
- ♣ –

Oliver Lombard
- ♠ 643
- ♡ –
- ◊ 973
- ♣ KQJ8742

FBI Trainee
- ♠ AKJ102
- ♡ 52
- ◊ K86
- ♣ A109

"Thanks, Director. Can I buy you a drink?"

"Mick, that deal was fixed. Lombard took the shuffled pack from his left, and switched decks. Yes, I know you didn't see it, because he's that fast. He passed the fixed deal to his right to be cut. You know a completed cut doesn't affect the order of the cards."

"Yes," Mick protested. "But it affects which side gets the winning hands."

"Both sides got a winning hand, Mick. If you and Ollie had been dealt the slam, the Senator might have pre-empted with 3♣ and good old Ollie would have overcalled with 3NT. I expect you'd have raised to 6NT, and now that wicked cross ruff wouldn't happen."

Mick peered at the four hands. "But does 6NT make?"

Boyles leaned back. "So I'm told, by the Department's top experts. It's a non-simultaneous double squeeze without the count, whatever that means."

Mick looked again. The Fibbies were right. Against 6NT, the ◇Q would be led. Declarer wins in dummy and cashes four rounds of spades and the ♣A, an essential play. The position would give declarer the opportunity to embarrass both defenders.

FBI 'Senator'
♠ –
♡ AKQ43
◇ 5
♣ 6

Michael McDeal
♠ –
♡ J10987
◇ J10
♣ –

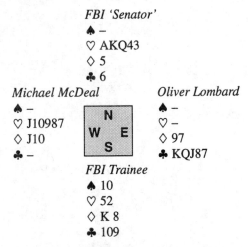

Oliver Lombard
♠ –
♡ –
◇ 97
♣ KQJ87

FBI Trainee
♠ 10
♡ 52
◇ K 8
♣ 109

The lead of the last spade squeezes West. If he throws a heart, South simply ducks a heart and claims. So West has to part with a diamond. Now declarer plays three rounds of hearts to turn the screws on East, the ♡Q lead squeezing him without the count.

Only a world class expert would find this play, particularly cashing the ♣A before leading the fifth spade, the key manoeuvre to avoid squeezing dummy.

So, whichever side held the big cards, the Club would be a big winner. Mick wondered which of the other pros had dreamed up such a diabolical deal. Probably Art Steinway.

Then he recalled his four heart contract against the two sheikhs. Of course! It was a hand Jeremy Flint had played in a Bermuda Bowl final. Lombard must have made the switch when he cut the deck.

He took a badly needed drink and said, "This is awful, Director."

"Sure it's awful. The guy has escalated from larceny to extortion, narcotics, murder, treason, and now – it had to come – cheating at bridge. And what's even more awful is that, if you try to quit the Lucifer Club, the Slasher will see to it that you have a nasty experience, like finding a black mamba in your jock strap."

Mick made a mental note to give up wearing jock straps. "And if I stay?"

"Then you'll become an accessory to card sharping. And you know what that will mean."

Mick's throat was dry. "The ACBL will take away my master points."

"You can bet your ass on it. Imagine starting again at the bottom in some penny-ante local event, and trying not to let your opponents see you write those words of shame on your tournament slip, 'Mick McDeal, unranked.'"

Mick shuddered. Rivulets of sweat poured from his face. "What do you want me to do?"

"That's my boy! We need a quarterback, Mick. We want you to find out what happens on the eighteenth floor, where they hide the cameras, the microphones, the bed bugs ...."

"Alright!" Mick yelled. "I've got the message. But what's in it for me?"

Boyles and Agent Florence exchanged glances. Jane placed her hand on Mick's knee and said, "After it's all over you'll be placed in our witness protection programme. You'll have a new identity, Mick."

"It's no use," Mick said. "As soon as I played bridge again they'd recognise my style."

"Our plastic surgeons can work miracles," Boyles said. "They'll give you a new face, a new body, even a new bidding system."

"I don't know, Director. I just don't know."

"And a million in cash, tax free."

"You're on. Swear me in, boss."

Boyles stood up and shook Mick by the hand. "Mick, I'm proud of you. We'll be in touch."

He left the bar, and Mick was impressed by the discipline of thirty agents as they rose in perfect unison and unobtrusively followed him into the street.

Chapter Five

Two days later, Mick partnered a famous band leader whose reputation as the worst player in the state was unchallenged.

Mick's left hand opponent was Rock Riley, the hero of a score of martial arts epics and victor of a hundred celluloid duels to the death. On his right sat the Obliterator, a muscular giant, who had just finished the eighth sequel to his original smash hit. It was called *Obliterator 9*. Years on location playing bridge while their stand-ins got beaten up had made them into crude but effective players. They used macho overcalls and Rambo pre-empts.

Mick soon had the chance to clinch a rubber with a far from cold club game.

North/South Game. Dealer West.

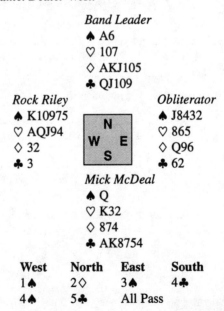

	Band Leader	
	♠ A6	
	♡ 107	
	◊ AKJ105	
	♣ QJ109	
Rock Riley		Obliterator
♠ K10975		♠ J8432
♡ AQJ94		♡ 865
◊ 32		◊ Q96
♣ 3		♣ 62
	Mick McDeal	
	♠ Q	
	♡ K32	
	◊ 874	
	♣ AK8754	

West	North	East	South
1♠	2◊	3♠	4♣
4♠	5♣	All Pass	

The bidding illustrated the robust style of the two superstars and Mick's determination not to let the band leader play the dummy.

Rock led his singleton trump. Mick pulled trumps and took stock. A successful diamond finesse would give him twelve tricks, but a superior plan was to lay down the ace and king of diamonds. He was safe if West won the third round, and he might find a queen doubleton with East.

Then he saw an even better line, so neat it should make Art Steinway green with envy. At trick three he called for a low spade from the table, his ♠Q forcing Riley's king of spades.

Riley began to look worried. With no good alternative, he exited with another spade and Mick parked a diamond on dummy's ♠A. Now he played the ace and king of diamonds and ruffed a third round. Two losing hearts went on the long diamonds, and the contract was home.

Suddenly he felt an excruciating pain across the top of his back. For a moment he thought the ceiling had caved in, but it was just the Obliterator giving him a gentle pat of congratulation.

"Mick, that was one helluva play. But what would you have done if I'd held the king of spades?"

Mick didn't need to think about that one. "I'd have ruffed it," he smiled. "Then I'd have drawn trumps, pitched a diamond on the ♠A, established the diamonds and claimed, hoping you guys didn't notice I'd palmed the spade queen."

"What a comedian!" Rock laughed. "Obby, I gotta have him in my next picture. We need somebody to play a real slimebag."

Mick revised his opinion of Riley. He'd figured him to be pretty stupid, but his humour was really subtle.

When the scores were agreed, the others went off to lose their customary fortune at roulette, and Mick took a trip to the Club's restaurant on seventeen, the highest number on the elevator control panel.

He ate a healthy meal of re-caffeinated coffee and double cream strudel and strolled back to the elevator. Then when nobody was looking he sneaked through the fire escape door. There were stairs going down and none going up. But a heavy door looked as if it led to the forbidden floor.

Then he noticed some scribbling on the wall by the door. He'd seen plenty of graffiti in his time, but this beat everything. It was a bridge deal!

North/South Game. Dealer West.

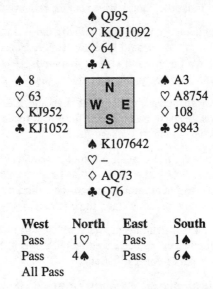

Spades QJ95
Hearts KQJ1092
Diamonds 64
Clubs A

Spades 8 / Hearts 63 / Diamonds KJ952 / Clubs KJ1052

Spades A3 / Hearts A8754 / Diamonds 108 / Clubs 9843

Spades K107642
Hearts –
Diamonds AQ73
Clubs Q76

West	North	East	South
Pass	1♡	Pass	1♠
Pass	4♠	Pass	6♠
All Pass			

Underneath the auction was a rather illiterate explanation of the early play.

Spade Led, Ace Spades, Heart Eight Ruffed

Suddenly Mick remembered the hand. It was from an obscure pairs event, but it had received a lot of publicity. And East was the late great Goldblatt.

He had won the trump lead and fired back a deceptive ♡8. Declarer ruffed, crossed to the ♣A, ruffed another heart, crossed to a trump and ruffed a third heart, revealing the subterfuge. Now he could still ruff out the ♡A, but was still a trick short. He fell back on the diamond finesse, but when that failed he was one down.

Other declarers had landed the contract by relying on the ruffing finesse in hearts.

Okay, it was a cute play by Goldblatt. But why had he recorded it in such a bizarre setting? Perhaps an epitaph! He must have known he was on his way to the roof, and used the deal to hide a message about his killer.

Mick stared frantically at the four hands. Then the solution hit him. The initials of the words scrawled under the auction spelled the name "Slasher!" He gritted his teeth, and tried the heavy door. It was locked.

"Michael McDeal, I do believe." As Mick heard the grating voice he whirled round to come face to face with the awesome Slasher. He hadn't been in such a mess since a dumb-ass splinter bid had landed him in a spade game with a void trump opposite jack tripleton.

"I was about to walk down," he mumbled, trying to keep the mumble steady. "I had to exercise."

He could see rolls of fat billowing over the Slasher's discreet Gucci gun belt, and made a mental note to give up cream strudel. But he knew that this was a man who could order his death with as little emotion as he ordered a kilo of French fries with his double helping of spare ribs.

The Slasher shook his head and said, "The way you were pushing that door I figured you wanted to walk up."

"I was just curious."

"Well remember what curiosity did to the kitty cat. The last bridge pro who climbed stairs found a brand new form of exercise. Sky diving. Only he forgot his parachute."

He banged a huge fist on the door. "I expect you could cut through that door, son. If you had an hour to spare and a laser gun. But then you'd come up against a concrete wall. I had it built as a memorial to poor Goldsplat."

"You mean Goldblatt."

"I know what I mean." The Slasher was enjoying himself. "The only way to eighteen is the elevator. You press 2-9 and 12 simultaneously, followed by 9-8-3. Think you can remember that?"

"Of course I can. I'm a bridge pro."

"But it won't do you much good, because we change the numbers every day. And those were yesterday's."

Mick ran down the stairs with the sound of mocking laughter ringing in his ears.

Chapter Six

At 8.30am the following morning, Benton Boyles picked up a doughnut, frowned and put it down again.

"This goddam case is killing my appetite," he grunted. "You're sure the elevator is the only way to floor eighteen?"

At 8.31am, Mick picked up Boyles' doughnut and ate it. They were doing breakfast with Agent Jane Florence in an FBI safe house, whatever that meant.

"I'm sure," he said. "You'll have to send in a task force."

Boyles shook his head. "We'd never get a warrant. Cheating at bridge isn't a federal offence."

Mick sipped his coffee. "I have a game plan, Director. It may be crazy, but I'd like to run it up the flag-pole and see if anyone salutes it."

"That's my kind of talk, Mick."

"I know. Well suppose I took a trip to the next state, stole a car and drove it back across the border. Is that Federal enough for you to bust into the Club and arrest me?"

"Damn right it is," said Boyles eagerly.

"But that only gets us into the Club," Jane interjected. "Not to the eighteenth."

"I'll be there" said Mick. "That's part two of my plan." He sat back, lit a cigarette and stared at Jane's legs, stretched out seductively from a brief leather mini skirt.

The Director smiled. "Mick, you're a prince of a guy. When the chips were down, I knew you'd put your country first."

Mick glowed with patriotic zeal. "Of course. And it will only cost you another million."

Boyles caught his breath. "Okay, you've got yourself a deal. Anything else?"

"Yes. I want to spend a few days with Jane. She'll need a crash course in high level bridge."

Boyles shot an enquiring look at Jane, who nodded imperceptibly.

"And I want you to meet two movie stars. " Mick continued. "They've been losing a wad at roulette and I think you should tell them why."

"Sure thing."

"And to complete the team, I think it's about time I introduced you to Art Steinway. He'll do anything we say, provided you can get him a free pardon from the ACBL."

❖❖❖

A week later, Mick was teamed with Rock Riley against Obby and Lola Fontaine, a dazzling redhead who he announced was co-starring in his next production, *Obliterator 10*.

At 9.00pm, Oliver Lombard dropped in to watch the play, as he usually did around that time. His presence was an essential factor in Mick's plan.

Lombard sat behind Obby, whose massive body provided the perfect shield for some slick sleight of hand.

Game All. Dealer West.

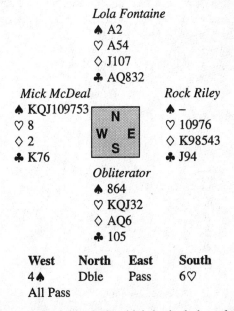

Lola Fontaine
♠ A2
♡ A54
◇ J107
♣ AQ832

Mick McDeal
♠ KQJ109753
♡ 8
◇ 2
♣ K76

Rock Riley
♠ –
♡ 10976
◇ K98543
♣ J94

Obliterator
♠ 864
♡ KQJ32
◇ AQ6
♣ 105

West	North	East	South
4♠	Dble	Pass	6♡
All Pass			

Mick was quite proud of this deal, which he had shamelessly fixed and switched packs in the true Lombard style. Since all four players were in on it, the Obliterator could give the cards a false cut to ensure that he would be declarer.

Mick led the king of spades on which Obby naturally put up dummy's ace. Normally, East would ruff this but the defence would now collapse. Taking advantage of the favourable lie of the cards, declarer would win the trump return in hand, ruff out clubs and draw trumps, ending in dummy. The long clubs would take care of both spade losers and the diamond finesse would bring him up to twelve winners.

However, Rock Riley studiously discarded a diamond at trick one.

Obby, who had been thoroughly coached by Mick, and was a disciple of the Stanislavsky School of Method Acting, regarded this card with obvious appreciation. Rock's play marked him with four trumps so there was no percentage in trying to ruff a spade with dummy's ace of hearts.

Was there still a way to make twelve tricks? Obby knew damned well there was – he'd memorised the deal the night before – but, like the Oscar nominee he was, he radiated hammy uncertainty.

He drew four rounds of trumps ending in hand and led the ten of clubs, intending to duck the trick to East. But Mick, reading the position with an expression of superhuman intelligence, inserted the king. Obby gave a grin of congratulation, but coolly won with the ace of clubs, played a diamond to the queen followed by a club to the eight, forcing East to take the trick.

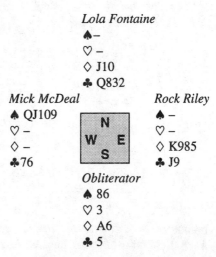

Lola Fontaine
♠ –
♡ –
◇ J10
♣ Q832

Mick McDeal
♠ QJ109
♡ –
◇ –
♣ 76

Rock Riley
♠ –
♡ –
◇ K985
♣ J9

Obliterator
♠ 86
♡ 3
◇ A6
♣ 5

At this point, Rock, refusing to lose face by being endplayed, threw in his cards with a gesture of resignation. Mick, with one eye on Ollie Lombard, decided it was time to get under his boss's skin.

"I'm going to send this hand to *The Bridge World*, he announced in his best journalistic style. "A deal at the Lucifer Club saw a succession of brilliancies by all the players. Rock Riley's refusal to ruff the spade ace would have destroyed many declarers, but the resourceful Obliterator seized the opportunity to show his steel. Taking in his stride McDeal's spectacular play of the king of clubs ...."

"If you've quite finished," Lombard interrupted, "I'll remind you that we have a club policy that none of our deals should be publicised."

"Sorry, Ollie," said Mick, who knew that Lombard couldn't afford to have his fixed deals seen by the bridge population. "I forgot."

The next hand was one of the most dramatic played at the club, possibly anywhere.

North/South Game. Dealer North.

Obliterator
♠ 643
♡ –
◇ 1098542
♣ 10963

Rock Riley
♠ –
♡ KQJ1076432
◇ QJ
♣ KQ

Mick McDeal
♠ Q1087
♡ A985
◇ 763
♣ 8 4

Lola Fontaine
♠ AKJ952
♡ –
◇ AK
♣ AJ752

West	North	East	South
–	Pass	Pass	2♣
4♡	Pass	Pass	4♠
Pass	Pass	5♡	5♠
Pass	6♠	Dble	All Pass

Lola's two of clubs opening bid was game forcing. After a crude auction she found herself in another spade slam, this time doubled, by Mick.

The king of hearts was led. Declarer could assume that, to justify the double, all four trumps were on her right. And she could only take one trump finesse.

She ruffed with the three of spades and began the process of shortening her trumps by under-ruffing with the two of spades. She successfully finessed the nine of spades, looking very learned when West showed out, and cashed the ace and king of diamonds, contriving to seem pleased at the fall of the queen and jack.

She took a sip of her iced vodka and cashed the club ace, which drew the queen from Riley. Praying that he held king-queen doubleton in clubs, she tried a second round, and almost purred when he captured with the king. With nothing left but hearts, he had to give declarer a ruff and sluff. Lola duly ruffed with dummy's six of spades, and underruffed with her five of spades! This was the position:

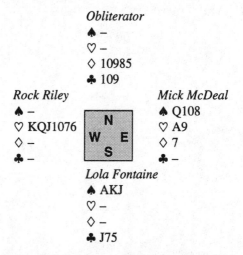

Obliterator
♠ –
♡ –
◊ 10985
♣ 109

Rock Riley
♠ –
♡ KQJ1076
◊ –
♣ –

Mick McDeal
♠ Q108
♡ A9
◊ 7
♣ –

Lola Fontaine
♠ AKJ
♡ –
◊ –
♣ J75

Now in dummy, Lola led diamonds until Mick ruffed. With a squeal of triumph, she overruffed to land a memorable contract.

At first everyone was speechless, especially Mick. He had arranged this famous hand, of dubious origin, specifically to infuriate Lombard.

"That was great, Lola," said Rock. "I just loved your kinky black under-ruffs."

Lombard had been watching the play with a taut expression. He calculated that Mick had lost over $18,000 in two rubbers.

Rock grabbed Lola's leg and fondled her knee. "You play bridge like a thoroughbred," he said.

Obby laughed. Or snarled – it was hard to tell which. "From the way you're groping her I guess you're ready for floor eighteen."

Lola's eyes widened. "What happens on floor eighteen?" she asked.

"Nothing that would turn you on, Lola". Rock said. "It's strictly men only."

"Oh, is it? Well I'm an equal rights freak, so you're taking me with you."

Lombard stepped forward, his smile strained but ingratiating. "Mr Riley's quite right, Miss Fontaine. The floor in question is for our male guests. Not that anything untoward takes place, you understand. It's rather like a gentleman's smoking club."

"Is that so? Well I happen to be dying for a smoke." She pointed at Mick. "With him. And what Lola wants, Lola gets."

Lombard looked shocked. "I'm afraid that's not possible. Mr McDeal is ...."

"A very juicy young stud, so I realise he won't come cheap. I'll tell you what, Ollie. If I can have him, you can keep my eighteen grand. For that I bet I could get Tom Cruise."

Lombard wavered, caution fighting with greed. Greed won, as Mick had foreseen. Rules were rules, but eighteen thousand bucks did a lot of bending.

"Okay," Lombard sighed. "I'll get someone to show you up."

Chapter Seven

Mick's master plan was going like clockwork. The security man played a complicated sequence on the elevator panel. Mick would have been terrified, but for the comforting bulk of the superstars and Lola's fingers massaging his lower back. They arrived at eighteen and stepped out.

Into Babylon.

Their feet sank into an antique Aubusson carpet. An eighty-foot corridor was lined with hand blocked silk covered with a row of post-impressionist masterpieces. The furniture looked like Louis XIV.

To Mick it just looked expensive.

They strolled into the lavish bar and chose a discreetly lit alcove. A voluptuous hostess came over, raised her eyebrows when she saw Lola, but quickly recovered her plastic, professional smile. Rock mentioned that drinks were free, so they ordered vintage Bollinger.

"What happens now?" Lola asked expectantly.

"The usual caper," said Rock, "is that a couple of girls drift over. Then if Obby and I take a shine to them we all take a trip down the corridor."

"And if you don't take a shine to them?"

"I don't know. It's never happened."

"Are the girls as free as the champagne?"

"Yeah. It sounds like bad business but, if you've just lost your shirt at the tables, a high class piece of complimentary tail sure sugars the pill."

The champagne arrived. Mick looked nervously at his watch. It was 9.30pm. He gave the others a pre-arranged signal to remind them that they were probably being watched and Lola nodded.

She drained her glass and rose from her chair with a suggestive wriggle. "Well, McDeal, I didn't pay eighteen thousand bucks for an evening of polite conversation. So let's haul ass down the corridor and find ourselves a love nest."

This was the crucial part of Mick's strategy, to get as far away as possible. Something nasty was about to hit the fan, and he had a brand new Armani jacket to protect.

It was 9.32pm when he and Lola locked themselves in one of the palatial bedrooms.

It was 9.33pm when the Obliterator and Rock Riley waved away two hopeful hostesses, and sent for a security man to take them down to the casino.

It was 9.35pm when the security man uttered his first scream of agony.

Chapter Eight

At 9.36pm, Benton Boyles and fifty of the Bureau's finest stormed into the Lucifer Club. He strode up to Oliver Lombard and waved a paper under his nose.

"This is a warrant for the arrest of Michael McDeal," he roared. "And you, Lombard, are about to tell me where he is."

"I've no idea," Lombard said, with the studied indifference of a man who had been through all this before. "I think he may have left the Club."

Art Steinway spoke up from a nearby table. "I'm pretty sure he went up to eighteen," he said, ignoring Lombard's glare of pure death.

"That's good enough for me," said Boyles. "Show us up, Ollie baby."

"I'm afraid the elevator is out of order," Lombard lied smoothly.

"Yeah? Well that's no big deal. We'll use the fire escape."

"I'm afraid the fire escape is out of commission."

"Gotcha!" Boyles laughed with fiendish glee. He dragged forward an officious looking man who brandished a subpoena.

"This, my oily friend, is the fire chief of this fair city. And he's about to bust you for a major safety violation. And we're about to search the building for more fire hazards."

As Lombard was led away, screaming for his lawyer, Boyles checked his watch and marched his squad to the elevator.

With perfect timing, the doors opened to reveal Rock Riley and Obby, holding a squirming security guard. The agents crowded in while the victim, encouraged by something Rock did to his spinal chord, placed a mangled hand on the control panel and painfully pressed the secret combination.

At 9:40pm, Jane Florence, still in the character of Lola, sat on the bed and gazed wordlessly at Mick. Her instructions were to protect him while the Bureau went into action.

Mick McDeal sat on the bed and gazed wordlessly at Jane. He also wanted to get into action, but was inhibited by knowing that the room was bugged.

But if he did nothing, anyone watching him might get suspicious. He was torn between modesty and necessity. His eyes strayed to her long, tanned legs, and modesty vanished.

He moved closer, and she locked her arms around his neck. They kissed. The earth moved. Bells rang. Neither of them realised they were alarm bells ringing to the defence of floor eighteen. They lay back, clinging together hungrily.

At last Mick had found something better than making a redoubled grand slam with a quintuple grand coup.

"Mr McDeal, I do believe!"

Mick froze. A .44 Magnum pointed menacingly at his midriff, and behind it was the evil figure of the Slasher.

"So you brought in the Fibbies," the Slasher said. "I guess I underrated you, McDeal."

"Yes, and this lady is a Special Agent." Mick's voice was pitched high with terror. "It's all over, Slasher."

"It's not over till the fat lady sings." The Slasher produced a pair of handcuffs and advanced towards Jane. "Do what I say, lady, or I'll blow a hole through your boyfriend's boxer shorts."

He manacled her to a bed rail. "And now, son, it's time for you and me to take a trip to the roof."

"For God's sake, Slasher! Not the roof!"

"Don't worry, McDeal. It ain't like poor old Goldblatt. I'm going for a ride in a helicopter, with you as a hostage."

He placed a powerful forearm around Mick's throat, and the muzzle of the gun to his ear, and pushed him out of the room.

There were agents everywhere, breaking down the doors, confiscating weapons, herding security people into the bar, and pacifying club members in various stages of panic and undress.

Benton Boyles stopped barking orders when he saw Mick and the Slasher. He raised his hand and a dozen guns were trained on the Club's security chief.

"Relax Mick," he said. "He won't dare pull that trigger."

"Are you taking bets?" Mick croaked.

"You'd better listen to your boy, Director," the Slasher grunted, and at a nod from Boyles the dozen guns were lowered, and Mick was forced slowly along the corridor and up the emergency staircase to the roof.

Mick could hear the sound of a chopper starting its descent. He tried to struggle free, but the huge forearm tightened, nearly choking off his breath.

Mick was about to pass out, when suddenly the grip slackened, and he fell to the ground, gasping frantically for air. He looked up and saw the Slasher being picked up by Rock Riley and the Obliterator. Slasher screamed horribly as they held him by his wrists and ankles and swung him backwards and forwards, gradually increasing the momentum until at last they released his body.

He went soaring over the edge of the roof to begin the swift, fatal journey to the sidewalk.

"It was an accident," said Rock.

"Yeah, " Obby agreed. "We were aiming him at the chopper."

His ordeal over, Mick staggered down the stairs, supported by the two super heroes. He thought fleetingly of his victory over the Club, his $2,000,000 and the Slasher's final satisfying scream.

But as he walked down the corridor, past the cheering federal agents, one thought dominated all others.

In the room at the end, Jane Florence was waiting, handcuffed to the bed.

HARLETT O'SCARA

3
HARLETT O'SCARA

Chapter One

When the last leg of chicken had vanished, the ladies retired to let out their eighteen-inch waists, leaving the house slaves to clear the barbecue tables, and the men to take their ease in the hot afternoon sun.

The conversation soon turned to the great event of the year, the long awaited bridge match against the North. Everyone knew it was an underhand scheme of Mr Lincoln's to whip the South and make them too scared to leave the Union.

What damned Yankee arrogance! Why, every man at the party was a born gambler who had learned to shuffle, deal and settle his losses, almost before he could walk. And their forcing four openings would bounce the Northerners out of every auction.

"Gentlemen," said Brett Rutter, "May I say something?" There was contempt in his Charleston drawl and insolent eyes. He sipped his mint julep and lounged elegantly near the magnolia bush, gazing languidly at the plantation where the negroes were singing spirituals and preparing the moist hungry earth for the cotton seeds.

"This is the South," he said, and his audience followed his gaze, weighed the evidence and nodded in agreement. "This is where men ride like the devil and leap high walls and to hell with what's on the other side! And that's how we play our bridge, with reckless jumps and futile sacrifices and to hell with what's above the line. Why, there's not one genuine bidding system south of the Mason-Dixon line. And not one practised partnership, because we Southern gentlemen change our lady partners after every rubber, as though we were at a society ball. We'll go to that green baize table like lambs to the slaughter".

A clamour of angry voices was raised against him.

"Why, one Southerner can lick twenty Yankees!" "No, fifty!" "God's nightgown! We don't need a bidding system to whip Lincoln."

Harlett O'Scara, eavesdropping from her hiding place in the Wilkes' stately oak tree, felt a strange thrill of excitement. She had heard such delicious scandals about the notorious Brett Rutter, the greatest lover, pistol shot and bridge player in Georgia. He was a big strong man of disturbing masculinity, who looked at a woman as though he knew exactly what kind of underwear she was wearing, and heartily disapproved of it. Folks said he was persona non grata, but Harlett thought he looked as American as anyone else.

Of course she realised that what he was saying was right. Fiddle-dee-dee! She was the best lady dummy player in the state, even if her bidding was as wild as a prairie rose, as Mammy was always telling her. But none of those fine gentlemen would let her play a contract. Except Ashby ….

As her thoughts turned to the noble Ashby Wilkes, she heard his golden voice remonstrating with the angry mob.

"Gentlemen," he said, heroically placing his slender, aristocratic body between them and the grinning Brett Rutter, "I must remind you that Mr Rutter is our guest."

The mob subsided. Southern pride was all very well, but it took second place to Southern hospitality.

"And please put away that rope," Ashby said. "I can't allow a lynching on the day I announce my betrothal to Miss Melody."

Harlett was numb with shock. So it was true! But how could her beloved Ashby marry that sugar-sweet, mealy-mouthed Melody, when everyone said Harlett O'Scara was twice as pretty?

As tears sprang to her eyes, she wondered what she could do to punish him.

Of course. She would enter the first round of the Atlanta mixed pairs. With Brett Rutter.

❖❖❖

Mammy's two hundred pounds towered menacingly over Harlett as she supervised her daily bridge problem.

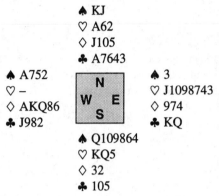

```
                    ♠ KJ
                    ♡ A62
                    ◊ J105
                    ♣ A7643
   ♠ A752          ┌─────┐          ♠ 3
   ♡ –             │  N  │          ♡ J1098743
   ◊ AKQ86         │W   E│          ◊ 974
   ♣ J982          │  S  │          ♣ KQ
                   └─────┘
                    ♠ Q109864
                    ♡ KQ5
                    ◊ 32
                    ♣ 105
```

Contract: 3 Spades

"Now, chil', you knows de contrack, you knows East bid hearts, an' you knows yo' left hand opponent (LHO) leads de two top diamonds. Den he switch to de club deuce. What you gwine do nex'?"

Harlett yawned affectedly. "Win and draw trumps."

Mammy's eyes rolled heavenwards. "Shet ma mouth! Yo' LHO wins wid de spade ace an' he leads a club. Den yo' right hand opponent (RHO) gets in an' he gwine give yo' LHO a heart ruff."

"I don't care,"Harlett sulked, "There's nothing I can do about it. "

"Nuffin'? Ain' Ah showed you de scissors coup till Ah's fit ter bust? You jes' wins de club ace, leads de jack o' diamonds an' you throws a club. Now yo' RHO cain' get in to play de heart. Yes'm. But dat LHO, he sho' ain' no expert."

"Isn't he, Mammy?" asked Harlett dutifully.

"No'm," said Mammy, delighted at the opportunity to prove her superiority over the fools who compiled bridge problems. "If he done switch to a club at trick two, dey's no scissors coup an' no nine tricks."

Harlett yawned again. "You're very smart, Mammy, but bridge bores me."

"Doan' do no good ter sweet talk me, Miss Harlett. You sho' fooled yo' paw and yo' maw, but Ah knows you is gwine in fo' de Atlanta mix' wid dat Brett Rutter. "

"And why shouldn't I, Mammy?"

"Cos he trash! Ah's seed him strip squeezin' dem ladies fit ter bust. An' dem psychic bids o' his … "

"Fiddle-dee-dee, Mammy! I can handle those."

"Well jes' you remember ter let Mist' Rutter bid de no trumps fust. He trash, but he is de bestest player of de dummy Ah's seed. An' doan' you bid no gran' slams. Dey is anti-pussentage. "

"Yes, Mammy. Now scoot upstairs and fetch my red silk dress."

"An' keep yo' eyes off dat Mist' Wilkes. He affianced ter Miss Melody. An' allus draw de trumps. Ah knows folks who is sleepin' on de banks of de Swanee fo' not drawin' de trumps."

Chapter Two

As Harlett sorted her hand for the first board she was conscious of Brett's pitying smile as he watched her with eyes that saw everything.

"If you will permit a suggestion, Miss O' Scara," he drawled, "It might be best if you didn't move your lips while you count your points. With my reputation as a Scallawag, I might be accused of taking advantage of the information."

Harlett blushed angrily, but pursed her lips tightly as she continued her counting. She looked with satisfaction at her powerful hand and vowed that nobody was going to prevent her from playing the contract. She had a forcing four bid!

Love All. Dealer South.

Brett
♠ KQJ8
♡ QJ109
◇ 98
♣ 762

Gaylord Ravenall
♠ –
♡ A8643
◇ QJ102
♣ KJ93

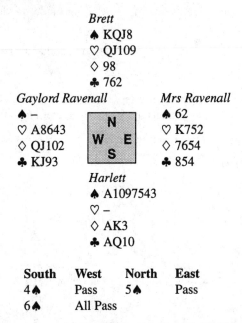

Mrs Ravenall
♠ 62
♡ K752
◇ 7654
♣ 854

Harlett
♠ A1097543
♡ –
◇ AK3
♣ AQ10

South	West	North	East
4♠	Pass	5♠	Pass
6♠	All Pass		

The brief auction was sophisticated for the Southland. Everybody who was anybody knew that devious Yankee auctions were not meant for ladies and gentlemen. Dixie slam tries were like marriage proposals; the gentleman asked and the lady invariably accepted.

Their opponents were the best pair in Georgia. Gaylord Ravenall, a fine card player, led the ◇ Q. Harlett immediately cashed her ◇ K and ruffed the third round, eliminating the suit, a manoeuvre which always gave her a glow of pride. Deciding to stake everything on the double finesse in clubs, she first played ♠ K and, when West showed out, called for the queen. Brett averted disaster by selecting not the ♠ Q but an unsolicited ♡ Q and before she could correct him, a low heart appeared from Mrs Ravenall.

With a gesture of frustration, Harlett was about to ruff, when she saw that the contract was practically certain. Ravenall could not hold ♡ AK, or he surely would have led one. So she artfully discarded a club. Ravenall won the trick and chewed his blonde moustache. Eventually he selected a low heart and his wife's king was ruffed by Harlett, who drew the last trump and proudly claimed.

"Beautifully played, partner," said Brett, but his maddening smile told her that he had controlled events by cynically misunderstanding her call for the trump queen.

Ashby would never have done anything so underhand, she reflected.

And she would have been one down.

For the rest of the tournament, Brett's brilliant card play, and his ability to steer all the difficult contracts his way, earned them top after top.

The last round saw them well in the lead.

Game All. Dealer North.

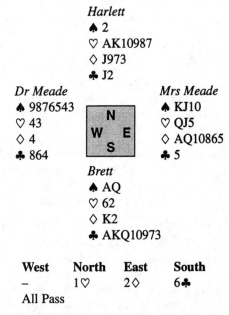

Harlett
♠ 2
♡ AK10987
♢ J973
♣ J2

Dr Meade
♠ 9876543
♡ 43
♢ 4
♣ 864

Mrs Meade
♠ KJ10
♡ QJ5
♢ AQ10865
♣ 5

Brett
♠ AQ
♡ 62
♢ K2
♣ AKQ10973

West	North	East	South
–	1♡	2♢	6♣
All Pass			

Harlett opened on her nine points without a qualm. Six card suits were meant to be bid, and if possible played in. Brett's 6♣ was most annoying, but after a long hesitation, she passed unselfishly.

Dr Meade, who had not spoken a word to Brett, led his lone ♢4 and his wife, who had not deemed Brett worthy of even a glance, played the ♢A. Brett, who was openly amused by their disapproval, and knew a singleton when he saw one, cheerfully dropped the ♢K. Mrs Meade, reading the doctor's lead as the top of a doubleton, switched to a hopeful ♠J. Brett won with the ace, ruffed a spade, drew trumps and cashed three more rounds of trumps to leave the perfect four card ending:

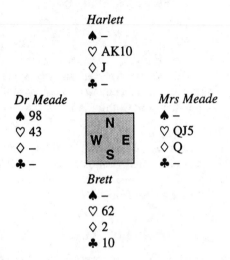

Harlett
♠ –
♡ AK10
♢ J
♣ –

Dr Meade
♠ 98
♡ 43
♢ –
♣ –

Mrs Meade
♠ –
♡ QJ5
♢ Q
♣ –

Brett
♠ –
♡ 62
♢ 2
♣ 10

On the lead of the last club, he threw the ♢ J from the table and Mrs Meade was mercilessly squeezed, or as she more delicately put it, discomforted. She threw a reluctant ♢ Q, but was mortified when Brett impishly produced his winning ♢ 2.

"I was sure the diamond king was single," she complained.

"I'm sure you were, my dear," her husband replied. "It was a *deceptive* play."

Harlett noticed that Meade spat out the word as if such a play was a device of the devil, and was overjoyed to have found such an accomplished partner. But she decided it would be wise to keep Brett firmly in his place.

"I believe six no trumps was a lay down, partner," she said sweetly. "I know my arithmetic is poor, but would that have given us a better pairs score?"

"It would indeed, Miss O'Scara," he said, glancing at the travelling score sheet, "but nobody else bid either slam, so we appear to have gained a thoroughly unpopular top."

"Really?" she said, as the Meades angrily left the table. "And how did Melody fare?"

"Ashby evidently languished in five clubs," he said, giving her his amused, appraising look. "And as he only just made it, his bidding showed excellent judgement. Of his playing ability, that is."

In the days that followed, Harlett, who had been taught that a lady should accept only candy and flowers from an admirer, received from Brett flagons of French perfume, an emerald to match the beautiful green of her eyes, a silk dress to match the beautiful green of the emerald, and a new bidding system.

Being a lady, she refused the bidding system. Then Brett showed her the intriguing possibilities of reaching contracts that were outside the compass of the simple ladies of Georgia, and she began to value it almost as highly as the perfume. Or at least one of the smaller bottles.

Chapter Three

Atlanta buzzed with excitement. The powerful Northern bridge team had arrived for the inaugural three-day match against the South, who had begun with a flurry of gallant charges, leaping to reckless slams which succeeded against the odds.

Then the tide turned. The North's bidding machine, with its measured, orderly advances, slowly wiped out the early gains of their gallant opponents. The South fought with rare courage, but a string of foolhardy games and vain sacrifices took their grim toll.

Dr Meade, who was Chairman of the hastily formed selection committee, rushed home after the first day's play to give his friends the bad news.

"Damn Yankees!" he cried. "They're all professional gamblers, not a gentleman amongst them. Why, when Gaylord Ravenall opened three no trumps, the next player turned to Mrs Ravenall and asked what her partner's bid meant."

"And what did Mrs Ravenall reply?" asked Melody, fascinated by this latest example of Yankee villainy.

"She told him not to ask impertinent questions!"

"Quite right," said Mrs Meade. "If we all knew what our partner's bids meant, it would take all the fun out of the game."

"Those carpetbaggers don't play for fun, Mrs Meade" her husband assured her. "When Wade Williams, or his partner – I'm not sure which – bid out of turn, they didn't ignore it like any gentleman would. They pulled out *rule* books."

"Rule books?" his audience echoed, almost in unison.

"It's true. Then, after a large dose of lawyer talk, Wade was banned from further bidding. The poor man couldn't say another word for the rest of the session."

"No!"

"He missed four slams. And one of them would have made."

"Poor Wade!"

"And as well as rule books, they've got convention cards."

"What in tarnation are they?"

"Lists of all their infernal bids that say one thing and mean another."

"But that's downright wicked," cried Melody, who had never told a fib in her life.

"I know. When Gaylord Ravenall opened a heart, there was a double on his left. His partner was having none of this, so she raised to four hearts, as any good Southern wife would, and there he played."

"Did he make it, Doctor?"

"He would have done. But he played for the trumps to be with the doubler. And every last one of them was with the lying scoundrel on his right who'd kept his mouth shut. When they told Gaylord that the double was informative, he said he certainly hadn't found it so."

"Good for Gaylord!"

Dr Meade sighed. "But they trussed him up like a Thanksgiving turkey on the next board. I made a note of it for you."

Everybody peered at the longest auction they had ever seen, and eagerly awaited the Doctor's explanation.

North/South Game. Dealer South.

Yankee Two
♠ KQ542
♡ K87
◇ 75432
♣ −

Gaylord Ravenall
♠ J
♡ QJ10
◇ KJ96
♣ KJ1087

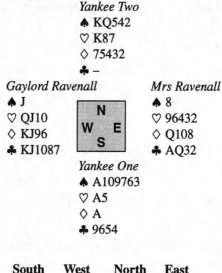

Mrs Ravenall
♠ 8
♡ 96432
◇ Q108
♣ AQ32

Yankee One
♠ A109763
♡ A5
◇ A
♣ 9654

South	West	North	East
1♠	2♣	3♣	4♣
4◇	Pass	5♣	Pass
5♡	Pass	6♣	Pass
6◇	Pass	7♠	All Pass

"Yankee number one," said Meade, steadfastly refusing to refer to him as 'South', "opened 1♠. Gaylord overcalled in clubs and Yankee number two bid 3♣!"

"But he didn't have any clubs," said a perplexed Mrs Meade.

"That's what he said it meant, Mrs Meade," said the doctor, who had never discovered her first name. "And the 4◇ was what they call a queue bid."

"Is that because it keeps everyone waiting?"

"I believe so."

"But what about that 5♣ from Yankee Two?"

"I don't rightly know. Perhaps he thought Yankee One didn't believe his 3♣ bid."

"But that 6♣ bid beats everything."

"I made a note of that one," Meade said. "It showed .... " He read proudly: "Interest in a grand slam and an undisclosed asset!"

"God's toothbrush! What in Hades is that?"

"I don't know and I was scared to ask. But they reached the grand."

"On twenty points?" asked Melody, who had just finished counting them.

"They made it on a cross ruff."

Ashby Wilkes, who had been listening gravely, spoke for the first time. "My friends, to lose this match would break the spirit of the South."

"I know that, Ashby," said Meade, "but how can we fight against rule books and convention cards?"

"We must fight fire with fire. Our team needs Brett Rutter."

"That black-hearted scamp?"

"The ideal qualification, Doctor."

"No decent person would sit opposite him," said Mrs Meade.

"One person would," said Ashby with calm certainty. "Harlett O'Scara. They've worked out a bidding system to drive the Yankees back to the Mason-Dixon line."

Meade looked doubtful. "Brett Rutter can't represent the South. It isn't decent."

"Decency, always decency." Ashby's tone was bitter. "Without Rutter our cause is as good as lost. And then we can bid farewell to decency, and all our other virtues."

Melody gazed at her fiancé with an expression of sheer, blind worship.

"Ashby's right," she said, "it's time to put aside our personal feelings. I shall go at once to see Harlett."

After Melody had been at once to see Harlett, Harlett went at once to see Brett, bringing Mammy as her chaperone.

"Lawsy, Miss Harlett, if you plays 'gainst dem Yankee card sharps, dey'll have you fo' supper."

"Don't be silly Mammy. I'll have Mr Rutter to protect me."

"An' if you ain' careful, dat Mr Rutter'll have you fo' supper an' breakfast."

Harlett had no idea what Mammy meant, but it sounded wickedly exciting. She tried furiously to think of Ashby.

If Brett was surprised at her visit, he was careful not to show it. When Mammy had been manoeuvred into a position from which she could observe but not hear them, he poured a brandy and a lemonade and asked, "Well, Miss O'Scara, have you come for another bidding lesson? Or are my forcing approaches too much for you?"

"Fiddle-dee-dee, Mr Rutter. Can't you ever be serious?"

"Not with you, my dear," he smiled, offering her the lemonade.

"There you go again," she said, taking the brandy and ignoring the loud sound of Mammy's eyes bulging.

"I've just come from Dr Meade's," she said airily. "He wants you and me to play for the South tomorrow."

Brett laughed loudly. "But whatever for? And why me?"

"The Yankees are too good for us, Mr Rutter. Dr Meade says the South needs our system. It's for the Cause."

"Miss O' Scara, I have an idea that I've said this before somewhere, but the only cause I know is Brett Rutter."

"Then play just to please me," she said coquettishly.

"And why should you want to take part in this absurd affair?"

She posed thrillingly. "Because I love the South."

"Harlett, please do not make the mistake of treating me like one of those calf-eyed young bucks who believe that you are sweet, innocent and artless. I know better. So answer my question and try to break the habit of a lifetime by answering truthfully."

"Very well, Brett." She looked defiantly into his dark eyes. "If we win, I shall be famous."

"And if we win, the South may secede from the Union."

"God's nightgown! What do I care if they succeed or not? As long as you and I do."

"It will mean war, Harlett."

"I'm sure it will mean no such thing."

He thought for a few seconds, and seemed to come to a decision. "Very well," he said, "I shall play. After all there is a great deal of profit to be made out of wars."

Chapter Four

When they arrived at the fine French Colonial mansion where the match was taking place, Harlett, radiant in her green silk dress with the matching emerald, was disappointed to learn that because of the emotions and tensions surrounding the event, kibitzers were banned from both rooms.

Brett, who was indifferent to the presence or absence of spectators, struck terror into the hearts of his opponents from the very first board. At this point the South were behind by more than 3000 aggregate points.

Love All. Dealer South.

```
                    Beery
                    ♠ 75
                    ♡ 9853
                    ◇ AQJ10
                    ♣ 1074
         Brett                      Harlett
                    ┌─────────┐
                    │    N    │
                    │  W   E  │
                    │    S    │
                    └─────────┘
                    McLaglen
                    ♠ AJ62
                    ♡ AQJ10642
                    ◇ –
                    ♣ 85
```

South	West	North	East
4♡	All Pass		

McLaglen and Beery, two hardened, pleasantly ugly gamblers of fearsome reputation, had to contend with an imaginative defence. Brett led the ♣K, followed by the ♣Q. Harlett overtook the second club and continued with the ♣J. When the huge Irishman ruffed, Brett discarded a small diamond.

McLaglen looked pleased as he led ♠A and a small spade, intending to ruff the third round in dummy and take the 'marked' trump finesse. Better odds than the fifty-fifty ruffing finesse, he thought. Harlett won the second round of spades and led a heart.

"Good try, me darlin'," McLaglen said. He confidently finessed the ♡J, blissfully unaware that the full deal had not been what Brett's play had led him to suspect.

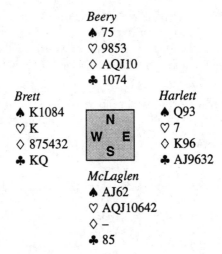

```
                        Beery
                        ♠ 75
                        ♡ 9853
                        ◊ AQJ10
                        ♣ 1074
        Brett                           Harlett
        ♠ K1084              N          ♠ Q93
        ♡ K              W       E      ♡ 7
        ◊ 875432                        ◊ K96
        ♣ KQ                 S          ♣ AJ9632
                        McLaglen
                        ♠ AJ62
                        ♡ AQJ10642
                        ◊ –
                        ♣ 85
```

When the ♡K appeared from his left, McLaglen turned to Brett in stunned amazement. "Do you by any chance play poker?" he asked.

"Occasionally," said Brett politely. "I never draw to an inside straight, or play against a man whose first name is a town."

"I can tell you're a man after me own heart," said McLaglen. "May I enquire whom I have the pleasure of addressin'?"

"Certainly," Brett lied brazenly. "I'm known as Charleston Joe."

In the other room, the heroic Gaylord had found no difficulty in making ten tricks, when the defence began with three rounds of clubs. He ruffed the third round with the ♡Q and, although this was overruffed, he now had sufficient heart entries to the table to establish the diamonds with a ruffing finesse.

Through a mixture of dazzling skill and outrageous luck, Brett had soon engineered a series of substantial swings, and McLaglen, who was musing over a bad result, launched his partner into a precarious contract.

Love All. Dealer North.

McLaglen
♠ QJ1098
♡ AK2
♢ 73
♣ Q86

Harlett
♠ 75
♡ J9864
♢ 1096
♣ J93

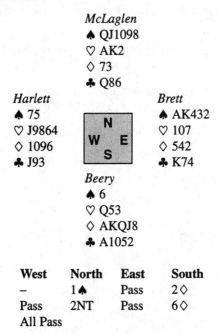

Brett
♠ AK432
♡ 107
♢ 542
♣ K74

Beery
♠ 6
♡ Q53
♢ AKQJ8
♣ A1052

West	North	East	South
–	1♠	Pass	2♢
Pass	2NT	Pass	6♢
All Pass			

McLaglen, mistaking the vulnerability, had shown 15-19 points with his 2NT rebid. Reasonably enough, the craggy-faced Beery leapt to the diamond slam.

Harlett led a safe trump. Declarer thanked his partner in a gravel voice noticeably lacking in gratitude. Calculating that the contract depended on finding East with the ♠AK, he won the first trick in hand, played the ♠6 to dummy's ♠Q, and could scarcely conceal his amazement when this held the trick. Hopefully, he continued with a spade. When this was covered, he intended to ruff, enter the dummy with a heart, lead a third round of spades and take the ruffing finesse. As the cards lay, this line would have succeeded.

But, when the ♠8 was played, Brett, with a faintly bored expression, ducked a second time! There was now no way for declarer to establish spades. Belatedly, he drew trumps and played a club to the ♣Q and ♣K, eventually conceding a second trick to Harlett's ♣J.

"Aw, shucks!" he said. "I shoulda pulled trumps before I started on spades. But why do I have to get defences like that?"

"Perhaps you did something wicked in a previous incarnation," Brett suggested helpfully.

Harlett only half comprehended what had occurred, but managed to cloak her ignorance with a mysterious smile.

After several flat boards, Harlett, once again fuming in the hated role of dummy, was forced to admire Brett's card reading.

Game All. Dealer South.

Harlett
♠ AQJ9
♡ Q765
◇ J2
♣ 932

Beery   *McLaglen*

```
      N
   W     E
      S
```

Brett
♠ K 7
♡ AK104
◇ AQ83
♣ 1085

South	West	North	East
1♡	Dble	3♡	Pass
4♡	All Pass		

Beery began with the ♣AKQ, McLaglen following upwards with the ♣4, 6, and J, and continued with the ♠2. Brett realised that he could not make ten tricks unless East had the ◇K, so he planned his strategy on this assumption. That left only ten points for West, so his vulnerable double must have been based on distribution. Brett decided to place him with 4-0-5-4 shape, and East with 3-5-2-3.

As he might find himself short of entries to the table, he took the first spade with dummy's ♠J and ran the ♡5, when McLaglen unwisely played low. When West showed out, Brett overtook the ♠K with his ♠A, discarded a diamond on the ♠Q, reaching a most satisfying six-card ending:

Harlett
♠ 9
♡ Q76
◇ J2
♣ –

Brett
♠ –
♡ AK10
◇ AQ8
♣ –

He successfully took the diamond finesse, cashed the ◇A, ruffed his last diamond with ♡Q, and made the last three tricks by finessing the ♡10.

The complete deal was:

Harlett
♠ AQJ9
♡ Q765
◇ J2
♣ 932

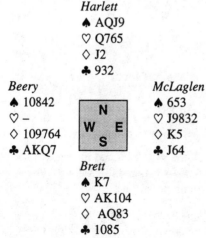

Beery
♠ 10842
♡ –
◇ 109764
♣ AKQ7

McLaglen
♠ 653
♡ J9832
◇ K5
♣ J64

Brett
♠ K7
♡ AK104
◇ AQ83
♣ 1085

Beery looked ruefully at Brett. "Charleston Joe," he said. "I think I could almost get to dislike you."

Brett beamed theatrically. "Sir, you would find yourself in excellent company, including half the North and virtually all the South."

"Pay no attention to my partner, gentlemen," said Harlett. "He just *tries* to make people dislike him."

Bett appeared devastated. "Do you mean I haven't succeeded?" he asked.

"Not with everybody," she replied, shamelessly fluttering her eyelashes.

The last board of the day gave Brett an opening to level the match.

Game All. Dealer North.

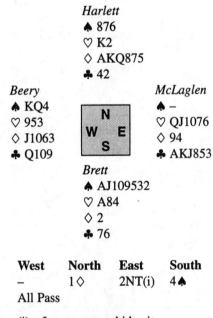

```
                         Harlett
                         ♠ 876
                         ♡ K2
                         ◇ AKQ875
                         ♣ 42
           Beery                         McLaglen
           ♠ KQ4              N          ♠ –
           ♡ 953         W         E     ♡ QJ1076
           ◇ J1063            S          ◇ 94
           ♣ Q109                        ♣ AKJ853
                         Brett
                         ♠ AJ109532
                         ♡ A84
                         ◇ 2
                         ♣ 76
```

West	North	East	South
–	1◇	2NT(i)	4♠
All Pass			

(i)   Lower two unbid suits

McLaglen overtook the ♣Q lead, and played two more rounds of clubs, shrewdly deducing that a ruff and discard would be of no use to declarer, and hoping for a trump promotion.

At this point, Brett, visualising something like the actual distribution, made the unusual and far-sighted play of ruffing in the closed hand and throwing a diamond from the table. The ◇A, ♡K and a heart ruff provided entries for three diamond ruffs in hand, leaving the following three-card ending:

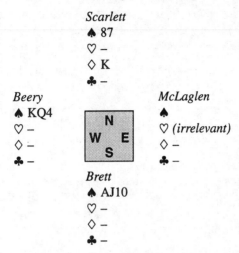

Scarlett
♠ 87
♡ –
◇ K
♣ –

Beery
♠ KQ4
♡ –
◇ –
♣ –

McLaglen
♠
♡ (irrelevant)
◇ –
♣ –

Brett
♠ AJ10
♡ –
◇ –
♣ –

Now Brett had an inferential count of the hand. When his ♠J appeared, Beery squirmed helplessly.

"I'm thinkin' I shouldn't have led the third club," said McLaglen. "Then Charleston Joe would have been an entry short for his trump reduction."

"That's true," Harlett agreed, lending credence to the remark with a brilliant flash of her lovely green eyes.

"Or I guess I shoulda led the ♣10," growled Beery. "Then I coulda dropped the queen on the next round to give you a count."

"I agree," said Harlett, repeating the flash, her eyes turning emerald.

"I would say you are being unduly hard on yourselves, gentlemen," Brett drawled. "When I ruffed in hand at trick three, it was because I had pulled the wrong card."

"Charleston Joe," said McLaglen, "It's plain to see that you've kissed the Blarney Stone. But I'll bet me last cent you're the only man it ever kissed back."

They compared scores with the Ravenalls, and discovered that the deficit had been reduced to a mere hundred points. Harlett took Brett aside and said, "Brett, I must say you played like a real hero."

"Why, thank you my dear. And may I compliment you on your part in a most satisfying session?"

"But that's the trouble, Brett," she pouted. "I had such a tiny part. I spent half the time following suit and the other half kicking my heels as dummy and watching you showing off your great coups and things."

"I see. So you're concerned that, instead of becoming famous, you will be condemned to read match reports referring to Brett Rutter and partner."

"Oh, Brett, you mustn't tease me. But you're so clever." She gently squeezed his arm and dimpled. "Isn't there something you could do to make me, well … just a little bit famous?"

"Harlett, you have more charm than the law should permit. I shall inform Dr Meade, the press, the Governor and the entire state of Georgia that it was I who kicked my worthless heels, while you single-handedly routed the Yankees. But you'd better learn what a grand coup is, my charming ignoramus. It will make your fibs more convincing."

That evening they dined with Ashby and Melody. Strangely, Harlett did not enjoy herself. Brett paid far too much attention to Melody, Ashby made no comment on her green silk dress with the matching emerald, and when she told him about her grand coup, he actually stifled a yawn.

For the first time in her life, she found him just a little tiresome.

The third day began with a succession of dull hands, which gave neither side scope to achieve a worthwhile gain. Then fortunes swayed like peach blossoms in the evening breeze. The skills of Brett and the luck of Harlett were counter-balanced by the flawed bidding of the Ravenalls in the other room.

Until Brett had a chance to strike a telling blow for the Cause.

Game All. Dealer South.

Harlett
♠ AJ432
♡ 84
◇ K3
♣ Q962

Sheridan
♠ 7
♡ KQ65
◇ J1042
♣ J1054

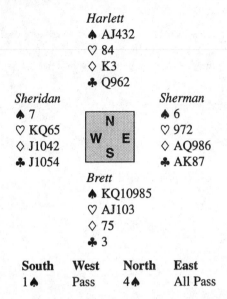

Sherman
♠ 6
♡ 972
◇ AQ986
♣ AK87

Brett
♠ KQ10985
♡ AJ103
◇ 75
♣ 3

South	**West**	**North**	**East**
1♠	Pass	4♠	All Pass

The North, utilising their superior manpower, were fielding two army officers, who according to rumour were being groomed for higher things – as if any Yankee was capable of higher things! Experience of Southern strategy was considered an essential part of their development. They looked confident against Harlett, who was clearly too beautiful to be intelligent, and Brett, who they knew had been expelled from West Point.

In the other room, Beery, also in four spades, had dropped the ♡10 on the ♡K lead, hoping forlornly for a heart continuation, but East's ♡2 deflected West from this course. The obvious diamond switch set the contract by one trick.

Brett looked shrewdly at Sheridan, a stumpy little man, with a forehead of no promise, and recalled that he had once claimed that if he owned Texas and Hell, he would rent out Texas and live in Hell.

Such a man richly deserved a lesson, and Brett was the one to administer it. He won the ♡K lead and, praying that East held the ♡9, smoothly returned the ♡3. Sheridan played low, and Sherman was forced to take the trick. He could not profitably attack diamonds and, whatever he did, Brett would have time to take the ruffing finesses in hearts and establish a winner on which to discard one of dummy's losing diamonds.

Sherman was not overjoyed. "You might have gone up with your heart queen, Phil," he told his partner.

"I didn't suppose that declarer would lead low from that combination," Sheridan replied. He turned politely to Brett. "Your strategy was brilliant, sir," he said generously. "I wonder why you left West Point so precipitously?"

"Do you?" Brett drawled, equally politely. "I often wonder I *stayed* as long as I did."

Soon Harlett found herself at the threshold of true fame.

North/South Game. Dealer South.

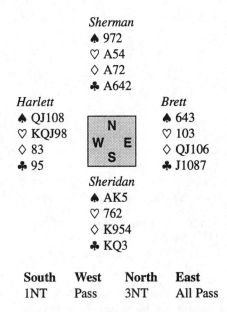

Sherman
♠ 972
♡ A54
♢ A72
♣ A642

Harlett
♠ QJ108
♡ KQJ98
♢ 83
♣ 95

Brett
♠ 643
♡ 103
♢ QJ106
♣ J1087

Sheridan
♠ AK5
♡ 762
♢ K954
♣ KQ3

South	West	North	East
1NT	Pass	3NT	All Pass

Harlett led her ♡KQ, Brett following with the ♡10 and ♡3. The cavalry man saw a glorious opportunity to ride into the Valley of Death and emerge, plus 600. He won the second round and quickly produced a small heart.

After greedily winning with her ♡8, Harlett was about to continue the suit, when she began to wonder why her opponent had played so strangely. She glanced at Brett for inspiration, but his dark face was inscrutable. One thing was for certain. If that damned Yankee wanted her to cash her heart winners, he could go on wanting. She was one of the fighting Irish O'Scaras, not some plaything for vulgar Northern trash.

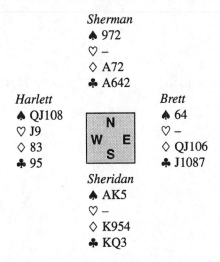

Sherman
♠ 972
♡ –
◇ A72
♣ A642

Harlett
♠ QJ108
♡ J9
◇ 83
♣ 95

Brett
♠ 64
♡ –
◇ QJ106
♣ J1087

Sheridan
♠ AK5
♡ –
◇ K954
♣ KQ3

A feeling of triumph surged through her, as she switched to the ♠Q and saw the dumbfounded expression on Sheridan's face. With the minor suits breaking badly, he could see no way to come to nine tricks.

"Bad luck sir," Brett smiled. "A clever attempted suicide, but my equally clever partner refused to become your accomplice. Had she continued hearts I would have been squeezed like a lemon."

Harlett had no idea what he was talking about, but was smart enough to lower her eyes demurely.

"The board will be flat of course," said Brett. "Mrs Ravenall must be south since she refuses to sit in any other seat. That lady has never heard of a suicide squeeze and, if she had, I'm sure she would reject it as unspeakably immoral."

Sheridan and Sherman were given diplomatic leave to make way for the return of the Yankees' most solid pair. The North were 790 points ahead when the last board was played, and Beery and McLaglen were confidently anticipating a huge winning bonus.

Game All. Dealer West.

Harlett
♠ 1076
♡ 842
◇ AJ10952
♣ Q

McLaglen
♠ A852
♡ AJ105
◇ K3
♣ J109

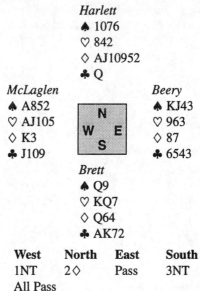

Beery
♠ KJ43
♡ 963
◇ 87
♣ 6543

Brett
♠ Q9
♡ KQ7
◇ Q64
♣ AK72

West	North	East	South
1NT	2◇	Pass	3NT
All Pass			

Harlett's vulnerable overcall, was almost indecently forward, but perhaps justified by the state of the match. Or the state of the Union.

McLaglen led a safe ♣J.

"Thank you, partner," said Brett warmly, as he regarded dummy's meagre resources as though they were the British crown jewels. "Small please."

The routine line was to win on the table and play a heart. Then if ♡K held, or if the defence correctly rose with the ace, but missed the blindingly obvious spade switch, and if the moon was made of green cheese, then a successful diamond finesse would guarantee the contract.

A lot of 'ifs', Brett mused, his lips drawn back in a fighting grin, his hard body poised like a panther waiting to spring. Besides, he respected his opponents. Holding ♠AKxx, McLaglen would have begun with the ace. So the top spade honours were probably split, which meant that West must hold ♡A in view of his opening bid.

Having completed this analysis in approximately three seconds, Brett called confidently for the ♠6! McLaglen played his ♠A on declarer's ♠Q, and returned a low heart, allowing Brett to steal twelve deliciously immoral tricks.

"You cunnin' divil," McLaglen exclaimed with the sincere admiration of one rogue for another. "But congratulations, Charleston Joe."

"He sure made a monkey out of you," Beery agreed.

"How do you think the scores stand?"

"I couldn't say, me boy," said McLaglen. "But I wouldn't like to live on the difference."

They soon found that the Yankees had gone one down in the same contract. Incredibly, the match was tied.

The referees were summoned, and decreed a four board play off. As it was a hot afternoon, they also decreed a mint julep break of unspecified length.

Chapter Five

Brett was quietly sipping his drink, when a steward brought him a message which said that he and Miss O' Scara were wanted urgently in the library.

Harlett, surrounded by admirers, all eager for news of her grand coup, was loath to leave. "Do we have to go, Mr Rutter?" she asked, watching him through the veil of her lashes.

"I believe we do, Miss O' Scara. Excuse us, gentlemen."

Brett and Harlett were shown to the library, where a group of tense men, obviously detectives, surrounded the entrance. One of them knocked, the door opened, and Harlett and Brett were ushered inside. Standing at the window was a tall beanpole of a man, who turned as they entered and politely inclined his head.

He was Abraham Lincoln, the President of the United States.

"Allow me to congratulate you, Miss O' Scara. And you, Mr Rutter. You have perfected the art of fooling all of the players all of the time. Your bridge is already the talk of the town, and will soon be the talk of the Union."

"Perhaps, sir," said Brett deferentially. "If there is still a Union after the next board."

"Quite so," said the President soberly.

"May I say, sir," said Brett, "that your presence here comes as something of a shock?"

"Of course you may, sir. Freedom of speech is still one of our most cherished privileges. But why should my presence shock you? If I remember the results of the last election correctly, I am President of the South, not just the North."

"A good point, Mr President. However the precariousness of that position is surely confirmed by the fact that you travelled here in secret."

"And I shall return with equal secrecy. But forgive my poor manners. I have taken you away from your drinks. Allow me to mix you both another. And please make yourselves comfortable."

Harlett sat with a puzzled frown as she watched Mr Lincoln prepare the drinks. Why was he doing it? Didn't he know that they had house slaves?

The President gave Harlett her glass. "I've been hearing about your grand coup, Miss O' Scara," he said, giving her a quizzical stare which reminded her uncomfortably of Brett. "Exactly how many winners did you have to ruff?"

"I've forgotten the exact number, Mr President," she said.

"It doesn't signify. I'm sure it was a play of great quality, yet here I am talking about quantity." He raised his glass. "To the Union."

Brett rose, but did not drink. Harlett drank, but did not rise. She hated politics, but adored mint julep.

Lincoln and Brett appraised each other in silence. The President was the first to break it. "Have you considered the consequences, sir, of your winning the last match?"

"I have, sir." Brett's lip curled. "I understand that a wave of pride will sweep through the South, who will promptly secede. There will be war."

"Which I'm afraid the North will win," said the President. "Unless in addition to developing your first bidding system you've built your first cannon factory? And I see from your expression that you haven't."

Brett's smile was sardonic. "Are you forgetting, sir, that one Southerner can lick fifty Yankees?"

"Come, Mr Rutter. You and I know that the number is no more than twenty. And one cannon can lick a hundred Southerners. I promise you, Mr Rutter, that the war will be a long and bloody one."

"I agree, Mr President. And if it makes you feel any happier, I promise not to fight in it."

"Thank you, Mr Rutter. But I would prefer you to promise to lose the four board play-off."

Brett's eyebrows rose. "You are asking me to betray the South?"

"No, Mr Rutter. I'm asking you to save the South."

He put down his glass and consulted his watch. "But I am keeping you from your bridge. Miss O' Scara, I wish you luck. Mr Rutter, I wish you would carefully consider what I have been saying."

"Mr President," said Brett, turning in the doorway. "May I ask you why you care for the Union so much?"

Abraham Lincoln pondered for some time. "Four score and four years ago, our fathers brought forth upon this continent .... " he began, and then broke off thoughtfully. It was a fine speech, but the world was not quite ready for it. Perhaps in two or three years time ....

Brett's face was an enigma as they slowly walked back. Suddenly he stopped, turned towards Harlett and held her by the shoulders in his warm strong hands. "Harlett, I don't expect you to understand this, but I have been thinking about what Lincoln said. We're going to throw the match."

She stared at him in horror. "But Brett, do you realise what that means? I won't become famous."

He laughed jauntily. "I love you, Harlett, probably because we are so much alike. Two selfish rascals. But somewhere inside me lurks that betraying sentimentality that is the South."

"Brett, I don't understand you. Are you really going to let the Yankees win?"

He leaned closer to her, his voice soft. "No, Harlett, you are." His kiss was like nothing she had known. She could feel it going right down to her toes.

The room was filled with excited kibitzers. Nobody could keep the glory-seeking Southerners from seeing at first hand the climactic triumph of their Glorious Cause. Brett and Harlett looked supremely confident; McLaglen and Beery were tense and wary.

Love All. Dealer South.

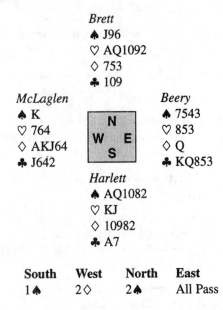

Brett
♠ J96
♡ AQ1092
◇ 753
♣ 109

McLaglen
♠ K
♡ 764
◇ AKJ64
♣ J642

Beery
♠ 7543
♡ 853
◇ Q
♣ KQ853

Harlett
♠ AQ1082
♡ KJ
◇ 10982
♣ A7

South	West	North	East
1♠	2◇	2♠	All Pass

Brett was relieved that he did not have to manipulate the bidding to allow Harlett to become declarer. His plan to let her throw the match was not inspired solely by his constitutional objection to being lynched, but by the knowledge that, if he misplayed a contract, the South would see through his duplicity. If a Scallawag like Brett let them down, they would claim he didn't count, so the South had really won.

Unknown to the players and spectators, the Ravenalls sitting East/West, had allowed the Yankees to make ten tricks in the same contract. Mrs Ravenall had begun with ◇AKJ and continued with a small diamond, ruffed by declarer with dummy's ♠9. When this held, it was not difficult for him to lay down his ♠A, felling the poor lady's bare king, and triumphantly making the rest.

Against Harlett, McLaglen started with ◇AKJ and noted Beery's ♣8 discard. He correctly guessed the result in the other room, and knowing that the smallest swing might be enough for victory, switched to the ♣2.

Harlett tried desperately to fathom the reason for this change of direction, but soon gave up. An expert would have deduced West's motive; all she cared about was making sure she got a bad result, just as Brett had told her to. She didn't understand a word of what he'd said, or Mr Lincoln, but she knew that in some strange way it was for the good of the South. Besides, Brett had such dark eyes, and such a hard, fine body. And her toes still tingled delightfully.

So she took the trick with her ♣A and tried to remember how she used to play trump combinations like this one when she was a little girl in Tara, learning the game on Mammy's knee. Of course! It all came back. With a mischievous glance at Brett, she blithely laid down the ♠A!

When McLaglen's ♠K floated fatally on to the table, there was an almighty roar from the entire assembly. Harlett looked in vain for a plausible way to avoid taking ten tricks. The board was flat.

At a signal from the jubilant Dr Meade, the band outside started to play 'Dixie', and Harlett used the diversion to break away from her admirers and say to Brett, "I tried, Brett, I really tried. I had no idea that trump king was single."

He looked at her, his face impossible to read. "I'm sure you hadn't, my dear," he said, "But your play was nonetheless deadly."

When the second board was presented, and the audience finally stilled, the Yankees bid ably to a small slam.

North/South Game. Dealer East.

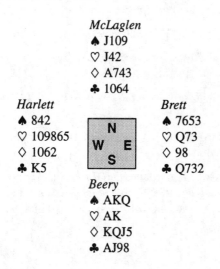

McLaglen
♠ J109
♡ J42
◇ A743
♣ 1064

Harlett
♠ 842
♡ 109865
◇ 1062
♣ K5

Brett
♠ 7653
♡ Q73
◇ 98
♣ Q732

Beery
♠ AKQ
♡ AK
◇ KQJ5
♣ AJ98

South	West	North	East
–	–	–	Pass
2♣	Pass	2◇	Pass
4NT	Pass	6NT	All Pass

At the other table, West led ♡10 against 6NT. Gaylord, playing with the dash of the riverboat gambler that he was, briskly led out ◇KQJ, overtaking the third round with dummy's ◇A. Then he made the mistake of running the ♣10 to West's ♣K. He won the heart return, and his carefully nursed ◇5 allowed him to reach the table with ◇7 and take a second club finesse. Unfortunately, the 4-2 break meant that he had to lose the fourth round to East's ♣Q.

The play was identical at Harlett's table until Beery demonstrated his superior technique. Instead of running the ♣10, he played a small club to the ♣J. As the cards lay, this would normally have guaranteed him his contract. But Harlett, seeing a chance to present the Yankee with a cheap trick, ducked shamelessly.

Declarer crossed to dummy's ◇7 and confidently ran ♣10, but when this lost, to Harlett's dismay and her bare king; there was no further entry to the table, and Brett's ♣Q unavoidably provided the setting trick.

The scores were still level.

Ignoring the tumultuous applause, Harlett gazed at Brett in mute appeal. Stubbornly avoiding her eyes, he commiserated with the sad-faced Beery.

"Bad luck, sir," he said. "Your play deserved a better reward."

"Thanks," replied Beery, and seeing that Harlett was surrounded by admirers, he leaned forward confidentially.

"Tell me, Charleston Joe. Is your lovely partner plum stupid, or as clever as a wagon-load of monkeys?"

Brett considered the evidence, "I believe I'm as much in the dark as you are," he replied grimly.

The third extra board almost persuaded Harlett that her every effort to lose the match was being thwarted by divine intervention. Had she known that Mars was the god of war, she would have blamed him personally.

East/West Game. Dealer North.

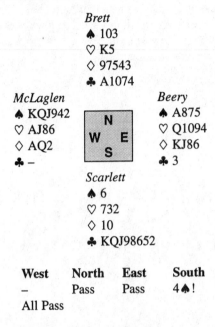

Brett
- ♠ 103
- ♡ K5
- ♢ 97543
- ♣ A1074

McLaglen
- ♠ KQJ942
- ♡ AJ86
- ♢ AQ2
- ♣ —

Beery
- ♠ A875
- ♡ Q1094
- ♢ KJ86
- ♣ 3

Scarlett
- ♠ 6
- ♡ 732
- ♢ 10
- ♣ KQJ98652

West	North	East	South
–	Pass	Pass	4♠!
All Pass			

Harlett, whose knowledge of psychic bids was as scant as her knowledge of mythology, produced the remarkable pre-emptive opening of four spades. As her card playing errors were being miraculously transformed into brilliancies, she was determined to see what vainglorious bidding would accomplish.

Alas, it accomplished the first gain for the South. McLaglen, playing takeout doubles over pre-empts, was forced to pass. Harlett, despite playing with dogged skill, made one trick, to sustain a penalty of a mere 450.

At the other table the auction was more orthodox.

West	North	East	South
–	Pass	Pass	5♣
6♠	7♣	Pass	Pass
Dble	All Pass		

The Yankees were three down in their 7♣ sacrifice, for a penalty of 500.

The South were 50 points ahead when the final board appeared.

The audience was spell-bound. Strong men chewed their cigars and clutched their brandy glasses with trembling fingers. Weak women wept openly and called for their smelling salts. The players could scarcely sort their cards. Only Brett seemed unconcerned, but the look he gave Harlett was harsh and uncompromising.

Game All. Dealer South.

Beery
♠ AQ1086
♡ 98
◇ QJ8
♣ Q42

Brett
♠ 73
♡ AJ6532
◇ 63
♣ 1073

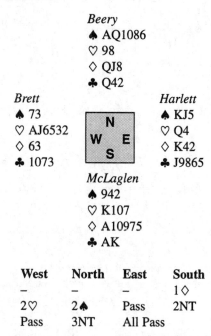

Harlett
♠ KJ5
♡ Q4
◇ K42
♣ J9865

McLaglen
♠ 942
♡ K107
◇ A10975
♣ AK

West	North	East	South
–	–	–	1◇
2♡	2♠	Pass	2NT
Pass	3NT	All Pass	

Brett's vulnerable overcall was a desperate attempt to sustain a match-losing penalty, but the Yankees proceeded to a reasonable no trump game.

Against the natural ♡5 lead, the contract would present no difficulties to a competent declarer, who would prefer the diamond finesse to the double finesse in spades, and make nine tricks exactly.

But in the closed room, Mrs Ravenall, after swooning with tension and being revived with sal volatile, relied on the spade finesses and finished with only six.

McLaglen won the first trick with his ♡K, and crossed boldly to dummy's ♠A. On this card, Harlett, in a final act of inspired lunacy, dropped a reckless ♠K!

Now McLaglen led his ◇ Q, hoping to induce an error. But Harlett, who had been religiously taught to cover an honour with an honour, perversely refused to do so. When she played low without a flicker, the Irishman won with his ◇ A and confidently ran the ♠9.

Harlett panicked. She considered ducking, but realised that her position in society would never survive three monumental errors in succession. Reluctantly took the trick with her ♠J.

She could still have saved the day by returning an innocuous club, but in the heat of the moment she advanced a fatal, match-winning heart.

The North were three down, the board was tied, and the Confederacy had won.

When the scores had been agreed, and the champagne began to flow, Harlett pressed relentlessly through the cheering throng to make her way to Brett, who had retired to the window to gaze out bleakly at the carefree people who were blissfully unaware that their precious way of life would soon be gone with the wind.

"Brett … " she began tearfully.

"Congratulations, my dear. It seems that your gallant attempts to snatch defeat from the jaws of victory were all in vain."

"But, Brett, I tried to lose, I really did. Surely you believe me?"

"I don't know what to believe, Harlett. You seemed to play like a blindfolded child, yet no master could have aimed more truly."

She drew a sharp breath. "And what are you going to do now, Brett?"

He continued to stare out of the window and said, "I'll buy some ships, become a blockade runner, buy cotton cheap, sell it to England at a dollar a pound, and become as rich as Croesus. Then, in an insane act of quixotry I'll join the Confederate army for the last great battle."

"No!" she cried. "Oh, my darling, if you go, what shall I do? We're in the final of the Atlanta mixed. What will become of me? Who will I play with?"

He turned to her with eyes that had never seemed blacker and said lightly:

"Frankly, my dear, I don't give a damn."

As he left, Harlett raised her chin with the defiance of a people who would never recognise defeat, even when it stared them in the face.

"Tomorrow, I'll think of some way to get him back. Tomorrow is another day."

THE BRIDGEFATHER

4
THE BRIDGEFATHER

Foreword

I sat against two members of the Bastinado family who controlled New York's prostitution and narcotics. My partner was my father, and the head of my family, Don Vito Cortisone, who controlled everything else.

We were enjoying a friendly evening of rubber bridge. The friendliness sprang from the wealth of affection and trust which existed between the two pairs, and the presence of the four armed bodyguards who sat behind each player.

Don Benito Bastinado thoughtfully rubbed two of his chins in an anti-clockwise motion, to show a fairly strong hand, with at least sixteen points. Rubbing the third chin would have shown nineteen or more. The demeanour of his nephew, Garrotto Bastinado revealed nothing, not because he had scruples, but because it was not his turn to bid.

In addition to their transparent signalling methods, deciphered several years ago by the other four families, the Bastinados played Standard American.

My father disdained all forms of questionable behaviour. He played bridge as he committed crimes – with unwavering integrity.

Love All. Dealer South.

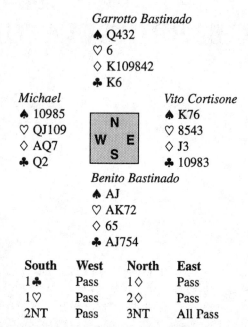

Garrotto Bastinado
♠ Q432
♡ 6
◇ K109842
♣ K6

Michael
♠ 10985
♡ QJ109
◇ AQ7
♣ Q2

Vito Cortisone
♠ K76
♡ 8543
◇ J3
♣ 10983

Benito Bastinado
♠ AJ
♡ AK72
◇ 65
♣ AJ754

South	West	North	East
1♣	Pass	1◇	Pass
1♡	Pass	2◇	Pass
2NT	Pass	3NT	All Pass

I opened with the ♡Q to the 6, 3 and K. With normal defence declarer was fated to establish diamonds and make nine tricks. But when at trick two he finessed the ◇10, my father, to whom outwitting fate was a way of life, impassively contributed the ◇3. Now declarer successfully finessed the ♠J, and played a second round of diamonds, on which I dropped the ◇Q.

Being the son of my father, I could almost read the mind of Benito Bastinado, as he tried to assess the distribution. He could not possibly place Don Vito with the ◇J 3, for, with such a combination, to refuse the trick would not be the action of a reasonable man.

So his thoughts turned to me, the untried son who had not yet made his bones, and he placed me with ◇Q7, ◇AQJ7 or ◇QJ7. Since the first two holdings would not allow him to establish the suit, due to the lack of entries, he decided to duck in dummy, hoping to see the ◇A hit thin air. I won and cleared the hearts, forcing Benito to rely on a favourable club position. When his ♣J lost to my ♣Q, a two trick set was assured.

When he discovered Don Vito's subterfuge, Benito Bastinado went purple with rage. The right hands of his eight bodyguards edged warily towards their shoulder holsters, but they were a split second behind the Cortisone soldiers, all trained bridge players who had foreseen Don Vito's subtle deceptive play. For a moment, the world seemed to stand still, as I watched the deadly tableau ....

Then my father raised his hand in a gesture of peace and the tension vanished. The two Dons embraced. The Bastinados praised the defence extravagantly. My father responded with true modesty. Such plays, his manner suggested, were commonplace.

And to Don Vito Cortisone, they were. Those who fell victim to his Sicilian spells, dug deep into their pockets and rued the day when he had forsaken the heady vintage of the tournament circuit for the rough red wine of rubber bridge.

It is in order to make known the events leading to that momentous decision, with its fateful consequences for the world of bridge, that I, Michael Cortisone, have allowed publication of the following chapters, previously omitted from the biography of the Cortisone family.

Chapter One

Don Cortisone's world was at peace. His *consigliere* and his *caporegemes* were functioning superbly. Competition had been ruthlessly eliminated. Business had never been better, his reputation never higher. The other New York families looked up to him with a respect bordering on awe. He had not needed to kill anyone for weeks, except for practice. He looked at all he had created, and found it good.

And Don Vito Cortisone was bored out of his Sicilian mind. He yearned for new worlds to conquer, fresh challenges to his genius for calculation, deception and the utter subjugation of all who dared to oppose him.

It was inevitable that such a man should be drawn, irresistibly, to Contract Bridge. The game had evolved from the head-to-head rubber bridge marathons, to a crowded calendar of duplicate events dedicated to the survival of the fittest. This was a creed with which Vito could readily identify. But, with his habitual caution, he decided to begin his career in the simple momma-poppa games of his own community.

At first he just sat and watched, absorbing the laws and the language of the game. Then he observed a hand which finally confirmed that bridge was his destiny.

Game All. Dealer South.

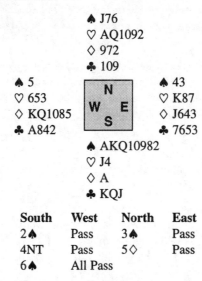

♠ J76
♡ AQ1092
◇ 972
♣ 109

♠ 5   ♠ 43
♡ 653   ♡ K87
◇ KQ1085   ◇ J643
♣ A842   ♣ 7653

♠ AKQ10982
♡ J4
◇ A
♣ KQJ

South	West	North	East
2♠	Pass	3♠	Pass
4NT	Pass	5◇	Pass
6♠	All Pass		

Even at that early stage of his development Don Cortisone was shocked by the barbarity of the auction, but its inevitable misuse of Blackwood was typical of the time, the place and the players.

South won the ◇K lead and promptly drew trumps. On the second round, West, a large woman from Genoa, banged the ♣8 on the table, with a meaningful glare at her small Neapolitan husband to indicate that this card was significant. Now when he came in with the ♡K he had no hesitation in returning a club to defeat the slam.

Don Cortisone's face showed nothing, but he felt an unfamiliar sense of elation. He would have taken the heart finesse at trick two. East would surely have returned a diamond, allowing declarer to ruff, draw trumps and discard his losing clubs on the long hearts.

And he, Don Cortisone, who had never played a card in his life, had seen the winning line in a flash.

The following day he showed the hand to Mr Van Donk, a respectable banker, who played regularly at one of the most exclusive bridge clubs.

Van Donk briefly regarded the sheet of paper and said, "Don Cortisone, is this a cunning trap? Declarer should simply take the heart finesse immediately, before West has a chance to signal in clubs."

"You are right of course, my friend." The Don's smile brilliantly masked his disappointment. "But I would be interested to know how many players in your club would declare this contract correctly."

The banker considered his reply. "Sixty percent. The other forty percent would draw trumps first. They are the life blood of American bridge, for they are the reason the rest of us win steadily."

Don Vito thanked him and left, reflecting that, if Van Donk's estimate was correct, he, a mere kibitzer, already had the potential to win at a leading New York club.

That night he began to devour bridge magazines. A week later, he felt ready to make his mark in the one cent games of the Italian neighbourhood. On the first day he broke even. Then he began to win with astonishing ease.

One hand, which was played in Vivaldi's spaghetti restaurant, gave him especial pleasure.

♠ Q10964
♡ AQ
◇ AK5
♣ K106

♠ AKJ532
♡ 62
◇ 43
♣ AJ7

Contract: 6 Spades

Vito never recorded the East/West hands because they were irrelevant and he was a confirmed minimalist. He sat South and played in a sound 6♠ contract. A low diamond was led, and he counted eleven top tricks. His twelfth might come from one of two finesses. He drew trumps in one round and was about to take the first finesse when he saw that twelve tricks were cold. Against any distribution! He cashed the ♠A and the other top diamond, cashed the ace of hearts and ruffed a diamond. He then exited with his ♡Q. He did not care where the king was.

Whoever held it would be forced to open up the clubs or concede a ruff and discard.

When he had made his contract he gazed around the table to see who had noticed his thoughtful play. The only acknowledgement came from his left hand opponent, a sharp-faced loan shark, who paid a monthly tribute to the Cortisone family.

"Congratulations, Don Vito, but allow me to point out that by finessing me for the ♡K and ♣Q you would have made an overtrick."

Vito gave the man his most chilling smile, calculated to reduce his every sphincter muscle to its component molecules. He did not know how much tribute the *bastardo* was paying but decided it was not nearly enough.

"It is generous of you to give me the fruits of your wisdom," he said softly. "But I favoured an elimination, a device I have found useful in the past and may use again in the near future."

The loan shark's bones turned to jelly. That night he did not sleep, and in the morning he sent the Don two cases of Asti Spumante with two dozen roses for Signora Cortisone. It was a month before he dared to play bridge again, but Don Vito unconditionally forgave him, raising his tribute by only a hundred dollars a week.

When Van Donk was shown the hand he was not impressed, but conceded that only thirty percent of his membership would find the Don's line. "But the other seventy percent are the life blood of American bridge," he said. "They are the reason why the rest of us win heavily."

And the Don knew he was ready for the next stage of his progress.

Chapter Two

Gunter Grubenhauser was a pale thin man with a shaven head. He was one of America's hottest tournament stars, and a great theorist. He had been invited to Vito Cortisone's house in Long Beach, and as he faced the Don in his expensively furnished study, he decided to charge the old Sicilian peasant an arm and a leg.

"First of all," said the Don, "I am grateful that a fine bridge player like yourself should spend time with an old Sicilian peasant like me. I realise that it will cost me an arm and a leg."

Grubenhauser tried desperately to conceal his shock. Was the man a thought reader? "Perhaps you could tell me what standard you have reached?" he suggested guardedly.

Don Cortisone shrugged modestly. "I manage to win steadily – against very poor players. But I have studied books, including your own." He produced Grubenhauser's standard work, *From Beginner to Expert in Six Weeks.*

Grubenhauser looked uncomfortable. "I must admit that 'six weeks' is somewhat misleading," he said.

"I agree," replied Vito. "It took me only ten days to master this book."

"Really", said the expert, profoundly shaken. "Then perhaps we should begin with some examples of advanced declarer play." He produced a well-thumbed notebook, flicked through the pages and showed his new pupil a criss-cross squeeze, a grand coup and the following hand.

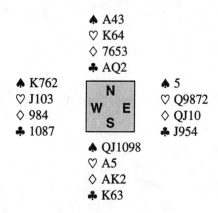

```
              ♠ A43
              ♡ K64
              ◇ 7653
              ♣ AQ2
♠ K762              ♠ 5
♡ J103        N     ♡ Q9872
◇ 984      W     E  ◇ QJ10
♣ 1087        S     ♣ J954
              ♠ QJ1098
              ♡ A5
              ◇ AK2
              ♣ K63
```

Contract: 6 Spades

"You are South, in a contract of 6♠. A diamond is led. How many tricks do you expect to make?"

Don Cortisone counted. "Eleven." he said. "I must lose a diamond and the ♠K."

"No," said Grubenhauser firmly. "You need not lose the trump king."

"Then perhaps West decides to cover my queen. This would make him unfit to play even at Signore Vivaldi's spaghetti restaurant."

"Follow me carefully. After taking the first trick, you play your ♠QJ. West, who has never eaten spaghetti in his life, ducks. Now you cash three rounds of clubs."

He watched the Don cross off the cards in his notebook, and decided to add the cost of a new page to his fee. "Now you play the ♡AK and ruff a heart. You cash your ◇A. Please show me the three-card ending."

Don Vito obeyed.

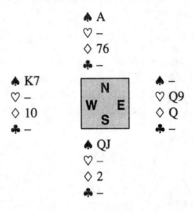

"Now Mr Cortisone, you are in your hand. What do you lead?"

"My small diamond."

"Correct. East must win and lead a heart. You play one of your spade honours and West squirms. His trump trick has been smothered, for you have executed a smother play."

Vito nodded. "Mr Grubenhauser, this hand is a miracle beyond belief. But in all the tournaments you have played with such great success, how many of these … smother plays have you personally contrived?"

The expert considered lying, but a glance at the Don told him that this would be unwise. "Well, to be honest, none."

"Then with all respect, if they are as rare as you suggest then to teach them to me is like teaching a Mexican peasant how to build an igloo." He smiled, pleased with his simile. "So now, Mr Grubenhauser, please show me something which will assist me if I should dare to sit down with players of your class."

Grubenhauser hastily put away his notebook and began to cover the serious business of high level bridge. He scribbled a hand.

♠ KJ9743
♡ 9
◇ AKQ42
♣ 7

"You open one spade, at Love All. Two hearts on your left. Two spades from partner. Three hearts on your right. What call do you make?"

Vito gave the question his full attention. "I bid four spades."

"Quite right, and you expect to make it. In Vivaldi's restaurant the bid is as inevitable as the spaghetti stains on the check tablecloth. But would you make the same bid against strong opponents? Partner has given you a single raise. It follows that they have as many points as you have, probably more. And similar distribution and strength. Over four spades they will probably sacrifice in five hearts. What then?"

"I might bid five spades."

"And you might lose three aces."

"Then perhaps I should double."

"And they might make five hearts. Mr Cortisone, you have a problem, but one of your own making. Now I would like you to consider what would happen if, over three hearts, you had bid a conservative three spades."

Suddenly, Vito Cortisone began to see the light. "They would bid four hearts. Then I would allow myself to be 'pushed' into four spades."

"And then?"

"They might double me."

"With very pleasant results. Of course they might still bid five hearts but you would be no worse off than if you had leapt to game in the first place."

The Don was beginning to enjoy his lesson, and he determined to extract the full value from it. "Is there not a danger that I will be left to play in three spades?"

"Of course," his teacher agreed cheerfully. "That is what makes bridge such an exciting game. But if you don't like danger maybe you should stick to the olive oil business."

His pupil smiled. He was not angry that this man should consider him a simple importer. This was long before a steroid hormone drug had been named after him, and he still treasured his anonymity.

"You are right. I know nothing of danger. But I believe I could get used to it. Please show me more clever tactical bids."

The master was warming to his theme. "You hold a fairly strong collection."

♠ AQ10864
♡ K42
◇ 5
♣ AQ7

"You open 1♠. You hear 2◇ on your left. Your partner raises to 2♠, and your right hand opponent bids 3◇. It is you to speak."

The Don considered his options. "I want to be in game only if my partner has a maximum hand, or can help me in hearts. So I would make a game try of 3♡."

Grubenhauser beamed. "Mr Cortisone, your answer is theoretically unchallengeable. However, you neglected to enquire about your opponents."

"Tell me about my opponents," said the Don dutifully.

"In the highest class, they would not be considered strong players."

The Don hesitated. "I would still bid 3♡, especially as it is theoretically unchallengeable."

"Would you? Well I would jump to 4♠, expecting them to advance to 5◇. Poor players often make ill-considered sacrifices, even if they are generally conservative. And if they leave you in 4♠, they might oblige you by slipping up in the defence."

Vito nodded thoughtfully. "And what should I bid against strong players?"

"You should only bid 4♠ if your left hand opponent is a confirmed overbidder. He will probably sacrifice."

"Probably?"

"In top level bridge, my friend, probably is all you get."

The instruction continued for several hours. When it was over, Vito Cortisone gave his mentor not only a generous fee, but also two cases of Asti Spumante and two dozen slightly faded roses for Mrs Grubenhauser.

Chapter Three

His lessons with Grubenhauser were going well, and Vito decided to risk
a few rubbers at Van Donk's club. Because he was venturing into foreign
territory he took with him his bodyguard, the terrifying Luca Tabasco,
whose savage presence sent waves of dread to everyone within a fifty-yard
radius.

As a kibitzer Luca was not a success. The Don's first opponents
deliberately misdefended to present him with two borderline games, and
then discovered that they had urgent appointments elsewhere.

"Signore," said Van Donk tactfully. "It must be very boring for your friend
to sit and watch. May I suggest that he waits in the bar as my guest?"

The Don looked doubtful, Luca looked malevolent.

"Do not worry," the banker soothed them. "I will personally protect
Signore Cortisone from all conceivable dangers, including flying pencils
and score pads. And our bar is well stocked with Chianti."

When the bodyguard had left, they played against O'Brien and Kelly, two
new arrivals whose nerves were still intact. At Love All, Vito dealt himself
a strong hand.

Love All. Dealer South.

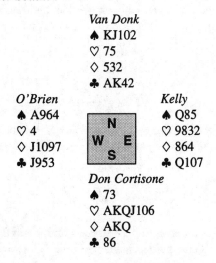

```
              Van Donk
              ♠ KJ102
              ♡ 75
              ◇ 532
              ♣ AK42

O'Brien                      Kelly
♠ A964          N            ♠ Q85
♡ 4                          ♡ 9832
◇ J1097     W       E        ◇ 864
♣ J953          S            ♣ Q107

              Don Cortisone
              ♠ 73
              ♡ AKQJ106
              ◇ AKQ
              ♣ 86
```

South	West	North	East
2♡	Pass	2♠	Pass
4♡	Pass	5♣	Pass
5◇	Pass	5♡	Pass
6♡	All Pass		

The Don was pleased with the friendly ◇ J lead, but calculated his chances at no better then even. Eleven tricks were assured, with the twelfth depending on correctly guessing the spade position. And the idea of giving an opponent an even break filled him, like Mr W.C. Fields, with extreme distaste.

Grand larceny was indicated. He cast his mind back to his war with the violent Beretta family in the days of prohibition. The odds were balanced until he created a cunning illusion of weakness where none existed, tempting his enemies into a fatally ill-timed attack. The resemblance between bridge and crime never failed to amaze him.

He took the first trick with the ◇ Q, deliberately advertising his strength in the suit. He crossed to the ♣ K and, as he explained later to Van Donk, took the trump 'finesse'. When this 'succeeded', he crossed to the ♣ A and repeated the 'finesse' with equal success.

To his great satisfaction West showed out, setting the stage for a piece of Sicilian sorcery. When he advanced a small spade, O'Brien, believing declarer had a trump loser and was trying to steal a trick with his ♠ K, stepped up with the ace. The Don won the diamond return and claimed. West was under the illusion that Don Cortisone's hand was :

♠ 7
♡ AQJ1096
◇ AKQ
♣ Q86

His opponents looked at him with healthy respect. He could see that they would never trust him to play a true card again. This was something he could turn to his advantage.

During the next few months, Vito Cortisone's bridge was divided between the better clubs and the crude local games in the Italian quarter.

It was at this time that he began to be known as the Bridgefather. Players would come to him for advice on how a hand should have been bid or played. Couples would beg him to arbitrate on disputes, some of which threatened not only a partnership but also a marriage.

One such husband and wife team was the Bolognaises. Mr Bolognaise was an honest, hard working baker, and a moderate bridge player, totally dominated by his shrewish wife.

"Tell him," said Mrs Bolognaise. "Tell the Bridgefather how you floored a slam so simple that my grandmother, God rest her soul, would have made it in her sleep."

"Well, I ... " Mr Bolognaise began.

"I'll tell him how," she interrupted loudly, pushing a grubby envelope towards the Don.

Love All. Dealer South.

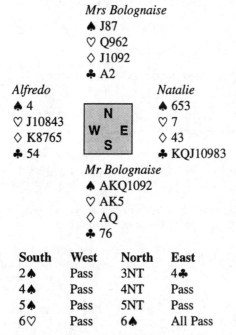

Mrs Bolognaise
♠ J87
♡ Q962
◇ J1092
♣ A2

Alfredo
♠ 4
♡ J10843
◇ K8765
♣ 54

Natalie
♠ 653
♡ 7
◇ 43
♣ KQJ10983

Mr Bolognaise
♠ AKQ1092
♡ AK5
◇ AQ
♣ 76

South	West	North	East
2♠	Pass	3NT	4♣
4♠	Pass	4NT	Pass
5♠	Pass	5NT	Pass
6♡	Pass	6♠	All Pass

Mrs Bolognaise filled her lungs ominously. "After Mr Bolognaise shows a very strong hand, I bid three no trumps, expecting him to be sensible and pass. Then Natalie, my brother's wife, has to butt in with her clubs and Mr Bolognaise repeats his spades."

"I see. And your four no trump bid?"

"To play. But he stupidly shows me three aces. So I bid five no trumps."

"To play?"

"Of course, Bridgefather. Then when he shows me two kings, I panic. I am afraid to bid six no trumps, in case he thinks I am asking for Queens." She paused, as if reluctant to confess her shame. "I knew it was stupid of me but .... "

"Please go on Signora," the Don said, with great compassion.

"I supported his suit."

The Don sighed. "You might have done so on the first round."

"I might, Bridgefather, if you had been my partner."

Don Cortisone's stern face showed his disapproval of such flattery.

"Tell me what was led," he insisted.

"A small club. So tell him, Bridgefather, about rectifying the count and the Vienna Coup."

The Don glanced with sympathy at Mr Bolognaise, who sat with his eyes downcast and his hands folded tensely on his lap.

"I believe your wife is suggesting that you take the first trick, draw trumps and lead a small club to rectify the count for a squeeze against West, who from the bidding may well hold four hearts and the ◇ K."

Mrs Bolognaise could no longer contain herself. "And then lay down the ◇ A, Bridgefather. Don't forget the Vienna Coup."

"Signora, it is not a true Vienna Coup, nor is it necessary in this case, as the simple squeeze is effective without it. But both lines fail if the ◇ K is with East."

He raised a hand, magically forestalling the next interruption. "The correct strategy, Signora, is a strip squeeze."

Mrs Bolognaise was shocked. Blushing deeply, she hastily pulled down her skirt to cover her plump knees.

The Don shook his head and continued, "Here is the seven-card ending:"

Mrs Bolognaise
♠ –
♡ Q962
◇ J109
♣ –

Alfredo
♠ –
♡ J1084
◇ K8
♣ 4

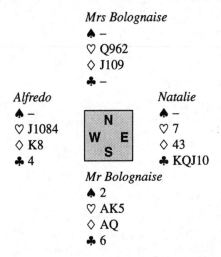

Natalie
♠ –
♡ 7
◇ 43
♣ KQJ10

Mr Bolognaise
♠ 2
♡ AK5
◇ AQ
♣ 6

"When declarer leads his last spade, West will probably discard a club. Now four rounds of hearts will compel him to lead away from his diamond holding, giving you your twelfth trick regardless of who holds the ◇ K."

He rose impressively. "As you know, I am in the olive oil business."

They both knew he was in the liquor business, the extortion business, the gambling business and all sorts of funny business, but they nodded vigorously to indicate that as far as they were concerned olive oil was his sole means of support.

"Somewhere in Sicily the olives are squeezed to produce the oil. But I know nothing about squeezing an olive. Why not?" He gave Mrs Bolognaise a grin which looked like a grimace. "Because the good Lord did not put me onto this earth to squeeze olives."

She gaped at him, her brow furrowed. "I'm sorry, Bridgefather, but what is that you are trying to tell me?"

He threw up his hands in despair. How could she not see the point of his beautiful parable? Did Jesus have trouble like this?

"Signora, your husband is a fine man. He bakes good bread, he never revokes, he supports your bids. But the good Lord did not put Signore Bolognaise into this world to squeeze opponents. For him, and I say this with respect, God created the simple finesse."

"Now I understand, Bridgefather," she said shakily.

"And when this fine man takes his finesse and goes down, do you know what you should say?"

She shook her head mutely.

"You should say 'Bad luck, my husband'."

"I will say it, I will say it!" she almost shrieked and, after kissing the Don's hand, bolted out of the room, dragging her husband behind her.

One of his supplicants was Mrs Valetti, the wife of an undertaker whose underbidding was legendary.

"Last night," she complained, "I knew we had a slam in spades but, as you know, I am from Napoli, so I explore for the grand. Three times I cuebid. Three times he signs off. So we stop in a small slam, with fifteen top tricks. Tell me what should I do?"

The Don thought carefully and said, "You must make him a slam try he can't refuse."

She stared at him for a full minute. Then her face shone with understanding. "I comprehend, Bridgefather. Thank you."

Two days later he received disturbing news and called at her house. Mr Valetti was indisposed but Mrs Valetti welcomed the Don warmly.

"I did it, Bridgefather. I took your advice."

"Signora, when I told you to make a slam try he can't refuse, I referred to Blackwood. It has its limitations but even the most cautious of partners respond to it slavishly."

He paused to give weight to his next words. "I asked you to bid four and, if necessary, five no trumps, Signora. Not to put the head of a horse in your husband's bed."

Nina Passionatta was astonishingly beautiful. She had a perfect oval face with exquisite creamy skin and full red lips. Her enormous eyes were innocent, yet sensual. Her figure reminded him in some indefinable way of his garden in Long Beach, especially its melon grove. For the first time in his life Vito Cortisone, normally strait-laced to the point of prudishness, was struck by the thunderbolt.

"Bridgefather," she said, her voice low and musical, "I wish to consult you about my boyfriend."

"I do not know whether … " he began.

"Oh, please do not worry, it is about bridge. You see, I have just moved to New York. I am a school teacher. Until recently I captained my college bridge team."

"Then you must be an expert," he said, vainly struggling to keep his voice steady.

"Well I have won a few regional tournaments. I mention this only because it has a bearing on my problem. Bridgefather, my boyfriend Carlo is a poor player. Yet he wants to be my partner."

"I see. And you fear that the difference in your standards will cause …. " He struggled for the right word.

"Acrimony?" she suggested.

"Exactly," he smiled. Usually he hated people to finish his sentences. But when Nina did it, it seemed to create a bond between them.

"I hoped you could come and watch us play. Then you could tell us whether we are …. "

"Suited?" he suggested.

"Exactly," she smiled.

"I do not think I could spare the time at present," he said slowly. "Perhaps you could give me some examples of your play. And Carlo's, of course," he added reluctantly.

"Of course, Bridgefather." She wrote out two hands, and the Don was pleased to see that even her handwriting was beautiful.

"This is my favourite deal," she said. "It was in the final of the college pairs."

♠ 654
♡ J6532
◇ 864
♣ 108

♠ AKQ103
♡ A7
◇ AKQ2
♣ AK

Contract: 6 Spades

"I am ashamed to tell you the bidding," she murmured shyly. "But I finished in six spades."

"I too would have bid the slam," he said, fully aware that in his present mood he would have agreed with her even if she had finished in eight hearts. "But tell me what was led."

"West opened with the ♡K. I won and played two top trumps. West showed out on the second round. The contract looked impossible. I had a certain heart loser and I could see no way of reaching dummy to take the trump finesse."

He nodded, and prayed that Nina had seen the need to cash her minor suit winners.

"So without much hope," she continued, "I cashed the ♣AK and ◇AKQ. Fortunately diamonds split 3-3. Then I took a deep breath."

Don Cortisone's experienced a divine vision of Nina Passionatta taking a deep breath.

"Then what did you do?" he asked hoarsely, suppressing the urge to ask her to demonstrate.

"I led my last heart, which West took with the ♡Q. I suppose I should show you the full deal?"

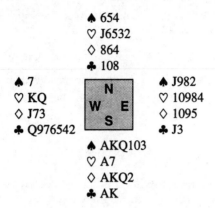

```
              ♠ 654
              ♡ J6532
              ◇ 864
              ♣ 108
♠ 7                          ♠ J982
♡ KQ          N             ♡ 10984
◇ J73       W   E           ◇ 1095
♣ Q976542     S             ♣ J3
              ♠ AKQ103
              ♡ A7
              ◇ AKQ2
              ♣ AK
```

"You can see, Bridgefather, that when West won the second heart he had nothing to lead but clubs. This was the four-card ending." She wrote with incredible speed, but the beating of Vito's heart kept up with her rapid fingers.

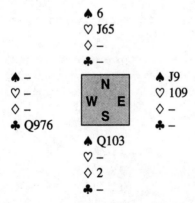

```
              ♠ 6
              ♡ J65
              ◇ –
              ♣ –
♠ –                          ♠ J9
♡ –          N              ♡ 109
◇ –        W   E            ◇ –
♣ Q976       S              ♣ –
              ♠ Q103
              ♡ –
              ◇ 2
              ♣ –
```

"I ruffed with dummy's ♠6. If East overruffed, I could claim. But he was a good player, so he discarded the ♡9."

"And what did you do?" Don Cortisone prayed that she had seen the need to underruff.

"I underruffed." she replied. "With my ♠3. I discarded my ◇2 on dummy's ♡J, and on the lead of the next heart, my ♠Q 10 was poised over the ♠J 9."

"A breathtaking coup." Don Vito murmured, still obsessed with his divine vision.

She smiled shyly. "You cannot imagine what a pleasure it is to show this hand to a genuine master."

Then her face fell. "Now shall I give you an example of Carlo's play?"

"No, that will not be necessary. I fully understand your situation." He now knew that she was not only the most bewitching girl he had ever met. She was his predestined bridge partner.

Chapter Four

By the end of the week Don Vito had arranged a series of games with Nina Passionatta. Her boyfriend Carlo had given his approval with immense enthusiasm as soon as the situation was put to him by the immense Luca Tobasco.

The Don was so grateful to the young man that he made him the manager of one of his most profitable enterprises … in Sicily.

The great bridge partnership began appropriately with a partnership evening at Van Donk's club.

Their first rubber was against two insurance brokers, McCallum and Scratchwood. The encounter was a milestone in the Don's bridge career, since it provided the first indication of his intention to dominate the game.

Game All. Dealer East.

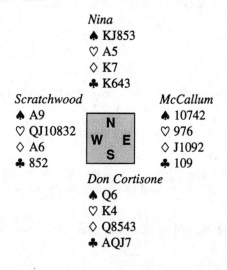

```
                    Nina
                    ♠ KJ853
                    ♡ A5
                    ◇ K7
                    ♣ K643
 Scratchwood                      McCallum
 ♠ A9              ┌─────────┐    ♠ 10742
 ♡ QJ10832        │    N    │     ♡ 976
 ◇ A6             │ W     E │     ◇ J1092
 ♣ 852            │    S    │     ♣ 109
                  └─────────┘
                    Don Cortisone
                    ♠ Q6
                    ♡ K4
                    ◇ Q8543
                    ♣ AQJ7
```

West	North	East	South
–	–	Pass	1◇
1♡	1♠	Pass	1NT
Pass	3NT	All Pass	

Scratchwood, a hatchet-faced man, and the club's most unethical player, opened with the ♡Q and the Don sensed that the broker had high hopes of defeating the contract.

He counted his certain tricks, four clubs, two hearts and two spades. He rejected leading the ♠Q because, if the spades did not break and West rose with the ♠A, he would clear the hearts, leaving declarer a trick short.

For a similar reason, the Don dismissed the idea of trying to sneak through a diamond. An alert West would put up his ◇A and defeat the contract unless the diamonds broke 3-3.

The Bridgefather completed his analysis and made his strike. Taking the first trick in hand, he advanced the ♠6. West correctly played low. Returning to hand with a club, Vito continued with a diamond towards the table.

This play saw the collapse of Scratchwood's ambitions. He was quite powerless. He played the ◇A, hoping his partner held the queen, but declarer now had his nine tricks.

"I'm glad I didn't double," said Scratchwood. "But I guessed three no trumps was laydown."

"Was it?" asked Nina innocently. "Then I'm glad you told me. I was about to tell my partner how well he had played."

"It was elementary after my vulnerable overcall," said the broker, with a sour glance towards Don Vito. "To be frank, I can't imagine why you paused for so long."

The Don regarded him curiously. Did the man have a sub-conscious death wish? If so ....

As the other tables were all in the early stages of a rubber, Nina and the Don again faced the two brokers.

Game All. Dealer North.

Don Cortisone
♠ AQ85
♡ K2
◇ 9
♣ K87652

McCallum
♠ 7
♡ J1097
◇ K1043
♣ J1043

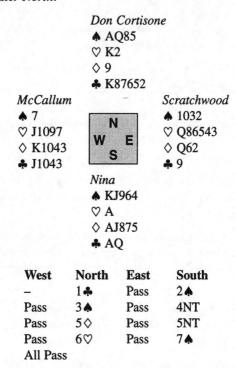

Scratchwood
♠ 1032
♡ Q86543
◇ Q62
♣ 9

Nina
♠ KJ964
♡ A
◇ AJ875
♣ AQ

West	North	East	South
–	1♣	Pass	2♠
Pass	3♠	Pass	4NT
Pass	5◇	Pass	5NT
Pass	6♡	Pass	7♠
All Pass			

Nina followed the then current trend of forcing immediately with her powerful hand. The Don disapproved of her subsequent unscientific bidding, but his manner betrayed nothing.

McCallum began with a solid ♡J, and Nina reviewed their prospects with qualified optimism. She could count thirteen top tricks if the clubs were 3-2, or even 4-1, provided spades were equally divided. At least a seventy percent contract, she thought. And received wisdom decreed that grand slams were the easiest contracts to play. But the Bridgefather had instructed her to believe received wisdom only if she received it from him. So she addressed herself to the problem of making thirteen tricks even if both black suits broke unkindly, leaving her short of entries to establish dummy's clubs.

At tricks two and three, she laid down the ♠K and ♣A, ignoring Scratchwood's hesitation before he dropped the ♣9. A small spade to the ace revealed the three-one break. Then came the key play of the ♡K, on which Nina discarded an inspired ♣Q. Now she was able to ruff a club. When East showed out she crossed to the ♠A to draw the last trump and ruffed another club in hand. Flushed with excitement, she played her ◊A and ruffed a small diamond. Dummy's clubs were now good.

Don Cortisone was unusually demonstrative. He said nothing, but his nod of approval spoke volumes.

They eventually won the rubber, but only after some questionable manoeuvres by Scratchwood. On one occasion he revoked, immediately apologised and left his discard on the table as an exposed card. But the information prematurely disclosed by the revoke enabled McCallum to find the only defence to defeat Nina's contract. The Don gave the insurance broker a look which would have chilled the spines of most men, but the broker continued to offend, thwarting declarer by taking shameless advantage of his partner's hesitations.

Even the Bastinados would never stoop so low, Vito reflected. Their illicit signals were a tradition handed down through generations of proudly fanatical card players, and their methods were so well known to their opponents that several of the younger Bastinados scrupulously included them on their convention cards.

A few days later, Don Cortisone received a visit from Van Donk. "My friend," said the banker, "I am pleased to tell you that the committee have decided to ask for Scratchwood's resignation from the club."

"But, he is a corpuscle of the life blood of American Bridge," said Vito. "He is the reason why fine players like you win so heavily."

Having bowed his acknowledgement, Van Donk continued. "We have not yet communicated our decision to Scratchwood, as it seems he is too indisposed to see anybody."

"I am sorry to hear that," said the Don, opening a bottle of wine. "Let us drink to his speedy recovery, and the hope that he was well insured."

"Several of his limbs are at present encased in plaster," the banker remarked casually. "He has no memory of the accident, but a man whose description reminds me of the charming Mr Tobasco was seen leaving his apartment."

Don Cortisone shrugged his shoulders. "Life is full of coincidences."

"That is true. But should you ever have a complaint against a member of the club, perhaps you will inform the committee."

"Mr Van Donk, I am sure I would never dream of complaining against a member of your fine club."

"I'm sure you wouldn't." Van Donk smiled. "That is why I am asking you to do so."

The Don could scarcely believe his ears. The pitiful laws of contract bridge included few penalties for unethical play and such punishments as there were were derisory. Could the fools not see that the Don's system of creative penalties was infinitely more effective? But he reflected that things would be different when he took control of the game.

He smiled at his visitor. "Of course I will," he said. "Would you like some more wine?"

Chapter Five

Since the Don's vast sphere of influence included the local education establishment, he had no difficulty in arranging for Nina to be given leave of absence from her school to receive advanced training. Her tutor was Gunter Grubenhauser, and her progress was almost as rapid as that of Vito himself.

It was with some confidence that they entered their first major tournament, the Fall Nationals.

In the first round, the Don played in three no trumps against world class opponents. Indeed he could not have made his wafer-thin game against lesser opposition.

When presenting the deal to Mr Van Donk, he did so from West's position:

North/South Game. Dealer South.

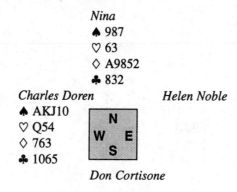

Nina
- ♠ 987
- ♡ 63
- ◊ A9852
- ♣ 832

Charles Doren
- ♠ AKJ10
- ♡ Q54
- ◊ 763
- ♣ 1065

Helen Noble

Don Cortisone

South	West	North	East
2NT	Pass	3NT	All Pass

Charles Doren led the ♠A. Helen Noble contributed the ♠2 and Vito casually dropped the ♠Q! Doren viewed this card with polite surprise. It could hardly be a singleton. And this Italian fellow was already gaining a reputation as a Modern Machiavelli. What distribution would justify such a bizarre play? He pondered, then smiled as the answer came to him. South must hold something like:

♠ Q63	or	♠ Q63
♡ A102		♡ AJ2
◊ KJ10		◊ KJ10
♣ AKQJ		♣ AKQJ

With such a holding the diamonds would be blocked, unless West could be persuaded to cash four spade winners. Now South would jettison his ◊ 10 on the fourth round and pray for one of the defenders to hold a doubleton ◊ Qx, his only hope. If he cashed only three spades, declarer could simply duck a diamond to East.

Grinning in wry appreciation of Vito's stratagem, Doren switched to a low heart.

The full deal was:

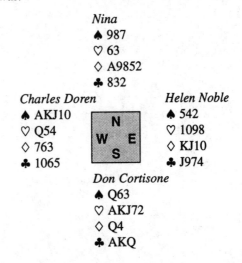

Nina
♠ 987
♡ 63
◇ A9852
♣ 832

Charles Doren
♠ AKJ10
♡ Q54
◇ 763
♣ 1065

Helen Noble
♠ 542
♡ 1098
◇ KJ10
♣ J974

Don Cortisone
♠ Q63
♡ AKJ72
◇ Q4
♣ AKQ

The heart switch was the only defence to give the declarer his nine tricks, but Doren took his setback with commendable sportsmanship.

"That was a masterpiece," he said. "It looks almost suicidal, but in fact you had nothing to lose. As it happened, you induced me to lead a heart, but had I continued spades or switched to clubs, you would still have had time to enter dummy and rely on the heart finesse. And as that would have failed, please accept my sincere congratulations."

Vito appreciated this tribute almost as much as the glow of admiration on Nina's face.

"You are very kind," he replied. "But I salute you in turn. Only a great player would have found such a disastrous defence."

A later round provided an opportunity for a defensive triumph, also against expert opposition. It became known as the Sicilian defence and has since been emulated by several masters.

Game All. Dealer East.

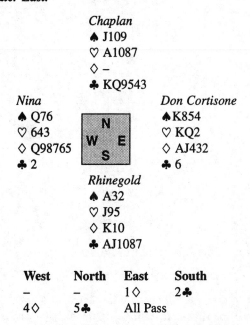

Chaplan
♠ J109
♡ A1087
◇ –
♣ KQ9543

Nina
♠ Q76
♡ 643
◇ Q98765
♣ 2

Don Cortisone
♠ K854
♡ KQ2
◇ AJ432
♣ 6

Rhinegold
♠ A32
♡ J95
◇ K10
♣ AJ1087

West	North	East	South
–	–	1◇	2♣
4◇	5♣	All Pass	

Nina's bold bidding could not prevent her opponents from reaching the good club game.

She led an orthodox ◇7, and Rhinegold calmly assessed his prospects. On the bidding there could be two heart losers, as well as a certain loser in spades. An elimination would succeed only if West could be prevented from obtaining the lead. And there was only one way that could be achieved ....

"Small spade, please," said Rhinegold, and the kibitzers blinked in amazement.

Then they saw the point of declarer's play. When East won with the ◇A, he would switch to a spade. Rhinegold would rise with his ♠A, discard dummy's last spade on the ◇K, ruff two spades, and return to hand with trumps, leaving the following position:

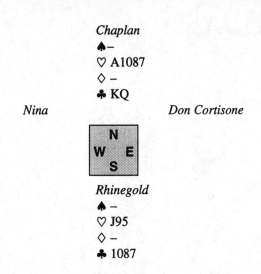

Chaplan
♠ –
♡ A1087
♢ –
♣ KQ

Nina   *Don Cortisone*

Rhinegold
♠ –
♡ J95
♢ –
♣ 1087

Now the lead of the ♡J would leave East without recourse.

Fine play, but routine for Rhinegold.

There was nothing routine about Vito's defence. When dummy's ♠9 was discarded on the diamond lead, he deftly contributed the ♢J. From his point of view the hand was almost double dummy, but it was still a great play. Rhinegold could no longer prevent Nina from obtaining the lead and pushing through a heart before the elimination was complete.

"Amazing," said Rhinegold.

"Thank you," said Vito, with a rare flash of humour. "I must confess I amazed myself."

"You must be the Signore Cortisone I've been hearing about," said Rhinegold.

The Don shrugged modestly. He briefly considered returning the compliment, but decided against the extravagance. He was too busy sorting his next hand.

The Don and Nina were leading the field at the beginning of the second session, and began with a series of good scores including a neat defensive combination:

Game All. Dealer South.

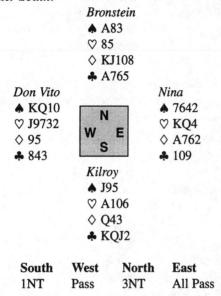

Bronstein
♠ A83
♡ 85
◇ KJ108
♣ A765

Don Vito
♠ KQ10
♡ J9732
◇ 95
♣ 843

Nina
♠ 7642
♡ KQ4
◇ A762
♣ 109

Kilroy
♠ J95
♡ A106
◇ Q43
♣ KQJ2

South	West	North	East
1NT	Pass	3NT	All Pass

Don Vito led his ♡3 to Nina's ♡Q. When it held, she continued with ♡K. Kilroy, a college professor, ducked learnedly. His plan was to win the third round, knock out the ◇A, and claim nine tricks if that card was with East.

But the third heart never came. On the second round, the Don dropped the ♡J. Nina was about to clear the suit when she remembered something he had told her earlier. "If I play an unusual card, you must consider doing something unusual." She considered, recognised the suit preference signal, and switched to a spade. Now nothing could stop the defence making two spades and the ◇A, to defeat the contract by one trick.

"That was a clever switch," said Bronstein, grateful for the excuse to ogle Nina.

"It was very clever," Kilroy agreed, examining the travelling score sheet. "So far nobody else seems to have found it."

"Thank you," she replied. "But my partner made it very easy for me."

Soon afterwards, a man strolled menacingly in the direction of the Don. His saturnine face did not betray the rapid beating of his heart, for he was an executioner, sent by enemies who saw Vito's obsession with bridge as a weakness to be exploited.

The Don had leaned forward to take a risky finesse when the killer's hand sped towards his shoulder holster. It never reached its destination. It was seized in the iron grip of Luca Tobasco, disguised as drinks waiter, while his left arm was grasped by another Cortisone soldier, recently qualified as a tournament director.

Few people noticed the strange trio marching towards the nearby exit, but the Don was pleased with his security, and even more pleased when the finesse succeeded.

Later in the session, Nina produced a deception worthy of Don Vito himself.

Love All. Dealer East.

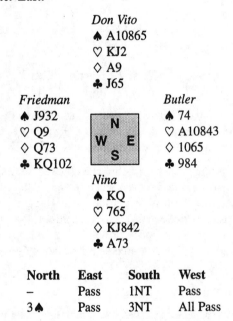

Don Vito
♠ A10865
♡ KJ2
◇ A9
♣ J65

Friedman
♠ J932
♡ Q9
◇ Q73
♣ KQ102

Butler
♠ 74
♡ A10843
◇ 1065
♣ 984

Nina
♠ KQ
♡ 765
◇ KJ842
♣ A73

North	East	South	West
–	Pass	1NT	Pass
3♠	Pass	3NT	All Pass

Friedman and Butler were two uncouth young men, noted for their competent play and poor table manners. After the ♣K lead, Nina could foresee some awkward communication problems so she ducked, dropping a deceptive ♣7.

The contract would have been defeated on a heart switch, but Friedman sitting West, read his partner's ♣4 as the beginning of a peter. Convinced that no sane declarer would forgo two sure club tricks by holding up the ace, he continued with the ♣2.

Nina won with dummy's ♣J, ignoring Friedman's grimace of disgust, and set about testing her long suits. She played her ♠KQ, crossed to the ◇A, cashed the ♠A, and finessed the ◇J.

Friedman won with the ◇Q but there was no way to defeat the contract. He did his best by cashing the ♠J and following with the ♡9, but dummy's ♡J forced East's ace, which was the defence's fourth and last trick.

Friedman scratched his head irritably and said in a grating voice, "Every other declarer will play the ♣A at trick one."

The Don recognised this as an attempt to denigrate Nina's line. "Oh, I don't know," he said reassuringly. "There are several other experts sitting South."

He bathed in the sunshine of his partner's smile.

When their opponents had slunk dejectedly from the table, she placed an affectionate hand on Vito's arm "Thank you, Vito." she murmured softly.

Nina was the only person who called him by his first name, and he struggled not to show how much he enjoyed it.

Respecting his diffidence, she diverted her attention to her scorecard. "We are doing well," she said.

"It would seem so," he agreed cautiously, refusing to reveal that he made them over sixty percent.

"There are two rounds left, Vito," she said, refusing to reveal that she made them over sixty-two percent. "What should our tactics be?"

"What have we been doing so far?"

"We have been playing good bridge," she smiled.

"That," he said, "is the best tactic of all."

The conversation ended abruptly as their next opponents arrived.

Game All. Dealer West.

Nina
- ♠ Q109
- ♡ KJ105
- ◇ K983
- ♣ K9

Lawford
- ♠ 876
- ♡ AQ7
- ◇ AJ10
- ♣ A1073

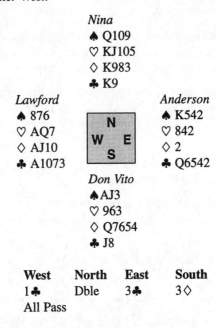

Anderson
- ♠ K542
- ♡ 842
- ◇ 2
- ♣ Q6542

Don Vito
- ♠ AJ3
- ♡ 963
- ◇ Q7654
- ♣ J8

West	North	East	South
1♣	Dble	3♣	3◇
All Pass			

Lawford, a world class player, led the ♣A. Anderson played low and Vito overtook dummy's ♠9 with the ♠J.

Lawford's permanent kibitzer sat between his hero and the Don, anticipating a clash of titans. At this stage, he predicted a one trick set.

Don Vito played a trump to the ◇K, and clearly should have continued trumps. However, at this point he could see little harm in leading dummy's ♠Q, until Anderson smartly covered with the ♠K, forcing declarer to play his ♠A prematurely.

A club towards the table fetched the ♣A from Lawford, who played a second round to dummy's ♣K. Now Vito was sorely pressed. He cashed the ♠10 and exited with a trump, won by West, who cashed his ◇A to leave the following position:

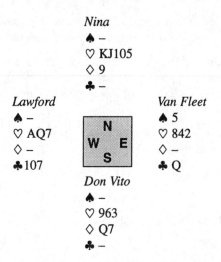

Nina
♠ –
♡ KJ105
♢ 9
♣ –

Lawford
♠ –
♡ AQ7
♢ –
♣ 107

Van Fleet
♠ 5
♡ 842
♢ –
♣ Q

Don Vito
♠ –
♡ 963
♢ Q7
♣ –

After mature consideration, Lawford advanced the ♣10. This presented declarer with a ruff and discard, but now declarer was subjected to a deadly one-suit squeeze.

The faithful kibitzer was content. The upstart Sicilian had finally met his match.

All his options seemed to be futile. Ruffing on the table would compel him to lead away from the heart honours. If he ruffed in hand and played a heart towards dummy, Lawford would be wily enough to play low. The Don could win on the table and return to hand with the last trump, but when the next heart was led, Lawford would win with the ♡A and produce the ♣7 for the setting trick.

Was there anything else declarer could do? Suppose he discarded the ♡10 on the ♣10? No, because when he subsequently led the ♡9 from hand, Lawford would calmly cover with his ♡Q and wait smugly for the lead from the ♡J5 round to his ♡A7.The kibitzer was grinning openly when Don Vito executed a sensational coup.

He ruffed in dummy and overruffed with the ♢Q! Now the lead of ♡9 ensured two tricks in that suit and his precarious contract.

"That was a brilliant recovery," said Lawford warmly. "You didn't choose the best line in the early play, but had you done so, then we would have missed a work of art."

The Don managed to look grateful, contrite, humble and triumphant – all at the same time. An achievement even more difficult than his ruff on ruff.

In the final round the Don and Nina sensed that they needed two good boards to be sure of victory. Their opponents were Sharp and Kean, two hotshot lawyers whose lack of ethics would have drawn an envious gasp from Scratchwood himself.

We must watch these two," said the Don, as he saw them walking towards the table. "I am told they are dangerous."

"And you are not?"

The encounter was to have a profound effect on the future of bridge.

North/South Game. Dealer South.

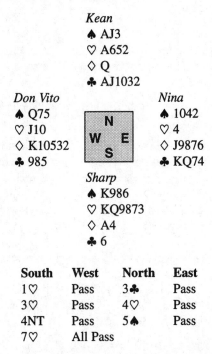

```
                        Kean
                        ♠ AJ3
                        ♡ A652
                        ◇ Q
                        ♣ AJ1032
        Don Vito                        Nina
        ♠ Q75          N               ♠ 1042
        ♡ J10       W     E             ♡ 4
        ◇ K10532                        ◇ J9876
        ♣ 985          S                ♣ KQ74
                        Sharp
                        ♠ K986
                        ♡ KQ9873
                        ◇ A4
                        ♣ 6
```

South	West	North	East
1♡	Pass	3♣	Pass
3♡	Pass	4♡	Pass
4NT	Pass	5♠	Pass
7♡	All Pass		

The ♡J was led, and the tall sinister Kean, who looked as if he was allergic to garlic and slept in a coffin, pondered his anti-percentage grand slam. It appeared to depend on the spade finesse or a favourable lie of the club suit. He took the first trick in hand and followed with the ♡9 to dummy's ♡A. The ♣A was cashed and a club ruff revealed that neither defender had started with the ♣KQx.

This was the position as Kean reviewed his prospects and his extensive repertoire of unscrupulous stratagems:

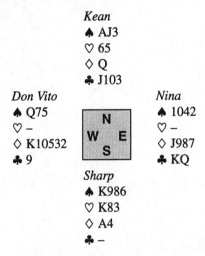

Kean
♠ AJ3
♡ 65
◇ Q
♣ J103

Don Vito
♠ Q75
♡ –
◇ K10532
♣ 9

Nina
♠ 1042
♡ –
◇ J987
♣ KQ

Sharp
♠ K986
♡ K83
◇ A4
♣ –

A normal declarer would now have resorted to the spade finesse, but the devious Kean could see another angle. Crossing to dummy's ♡5, on which the ◇2 appeared from West, he continued with the ◇Q and brazenly discarded a spade!

He correctly reasoned that East, holding ◇K without the knave, might choose not to cover. When the ◇3 appeared from the Don it was time for the second phase of his devilish plan.

"Sorry, I pulled the wrong card," he lied, smoothly replacing his spade with ◇4. "I have a diamond."

"In fact I think you have two," the Don smiled, replacing his own ◇3 with the king, for the setting trick. "I believe that I too have the right to change my card."

Sharp was forced to admire his opponent's table presence. Had the Don played his ◇K to start with, he would have replaced his ♠6 with the ◇A and made his contract with a successful spade finesse. But his admiration did not deter him from continuing his sharp practice on the final, fateful board.

East/West Game. Dealer South.

Nina
♠ QJ4
♡ J1085
◇ KQJ102
♣ 6

Kean
♠ A9862
♡ 2
◇ 96
♣ AQJ85

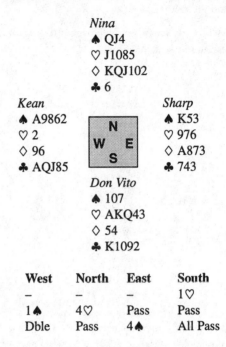

Sharp
♠ K53
♡ 976
◇ A873
♣ 743

Don Vito
♠ 107
♡ AKQ43
◇ 54
♣ K1092

West	North	East	South
–	–	–	1♡
1♠	4♡	Pass	Pass
Dble	Pass	4♠	All Pass

When Nina raised her partner's opening bid to four hearts, she would have silenced many opponents but Sharp passed after a revealing hesitation. This meant that he was considering either a penalty double or a bid of four spades. Kean demonstrated their supreme partnership understanding by making a slow double, which catered admirably for either option.

Four spades proved unstoppable, and prevented the Italian pair from winning the competition.

Scorning the idea of lodging a formal complaint, the Bridgefather stared first at Sharp and then at Kean, with an expression which made each of them feel he was being measured for a cement overcoat.

But Don Vito had in mind something more imaginative ....

Chapter Six

Two months went by. The Don and his young partner were on the verge of major honours. Then, one morning, Vito received a visit from an important man, a genuine member of the *pezzonavanti*, one ranked high in the all-powerful American Contract Bridge League.

The first few minutes passed agreeably. The Don plied the official with wine. The official plied him with compliments. Then he came to the point of the meeting.

"Signore Cortisone," he said. "Two of our members, Mr Sharp and Mr Kean, had a successful law practice. But in eight brief weeks their fortunes have changed. They are losing case after case. It is as if the judges, who I gather are all close friends of yours, are united in a vendetta against them."

"That is unfortunate," the Don said agreeably. "But why do you come to me?"

His guest sighed. "I thought perhaps God was punishing them for their coffee-house tactics. I would of course never criticise God, but I would have thought a long succession of bottoms would have been punishment enough."

Don Cortisone said nothing. He waited to discover his opponent's strength.

"Of course," the official went on, "Sharp and Kean might have met with an unfortunate accident, like that unpleasant Scratchwood. Or vanished into thin air, like that sinister spectator in the Fall Nationals."

"Now I see," Vito said, awed by the quality of the League's intelligence and feigning a sudden understanding. "You are connecting these incidents with me."

"Do not misunderstand me, Signore Cortisone. The ACBL are pleased with the improvement in ethics. But we are disturbed by the alarming decline in our membership."

The Don rose with great dignity. "I believe the time has come for plain speaking. When I came to this great country I soon found that the strong made the rules, and broke them without hesitation and without fear. When I saw that this was so I decided to become even stronger. So my olive oil business prospered, and I decided to retire and enter the world of bridge."

He moved to the window and looked out into his garden, but the melon grove reminded him uncomfortably of Nina, and he turned back towards his visitor.

"I have watched Sharp and Kean, with their shrewd legal brains, make fools of opponents and directors. But your League does nothing."

"That is not true. We have our eyes on Sharp and Kean."

"But I have done your job for you. In a few months they will not be able to afford their annual membership, let alone their card fees."

The official stood up. "Signore, I have made our position clear. You must in future leave retribution to us. And, in the meantime, it might be advisable for you and your bodyguards to take a rest from tournament bridge."

He walked to the door, bowed politely and left.

Vito stared after him in stunned disbelief. How could someone so lacking in reason have risen to a position of such power? Did he not realise he had just signed his own death warrant?

Then the Don stilled his icy rage. Reluctantly, he admired the man's courage. Besides, his death would solve nothing. There would be a hundred others ready to take his place.

So Vito would strike not at the League, but at the country which had permitted such people to control its greatest game.

And he could afford to wait. Vengeance was a dish best tasted cold.

Several years later, Vito sat in his study and regarded his beautiful Bridge-daughter with deep satisfaction. His retirement from serious competition had allowed him to employ all his energies to nurture her God-given talent, and Nina had rewarded him by winning every major honour in the ladies' game.

Together, they read for the third time a letter from his agent in Italy, a letter which foreshadowed his long awaited revenge, serpentine in its conception, tigerish in its execution.

It contained names of the men who, with the Don gently pulling the invisible strings, would wrest supremacy from the greatest bridge nation on earth.

"Avarelli, Belladonna, Chiaradia, Forquet, Garozzo .... "